SUPERVISION OF CONSTRUCTION

SUPERVISION OF CONSTRUCTION

Proceedings of a symposium organized by the Institution of Civil Engineers and held in London, 7–8 June 1984

THOMAS TELFORD LTD, LONDON, 1985

Published for the Institution of Civil Engineers by Thomas Telford Limited, PO Box 101, 26–34 Old Street, London, EC1P 1JH.

First published 1985.

Organizing Committee: E. M. O'Leary, P. Dann, D. Dennington, H. B. Gould and D. E. Neale.

ISBN: 0 7277 0225 4

Printed in Great Britain by Billings and Sons Ltd, Worcester

Contents

1 The ICE and FIDIC Conditions of Contract and background laws

M. W. ABRAHAMSON, LLB, Solicitor McCann Fitzgerald Sutton Dudley, Dublin

SYNOPSIS: There are practical questions about the law to which supervisors need to know the answers if good construction is to have its proper priority. The answers depend on unsatisfactory foundations of the law of negligence in theory and reality and a superstructure of standard contract terms and industry practice, which are discussed. A largely unsuccessful attempt is made to supply useful answers.

The Problems: I am qualified to write on supervisors' problems only because the legal profession is a supervisors' problem. The first aim of a supervisor should be to produce works that are satisfactory, and the second to be clear of the law if they are not. This conference would be less necessary, and I certainly would not have been invited to it, but for growing confusion or even reversal of those priorities, partly due to faulty supervision of law by lawyers. The aim here is to try to give you the flavour of what happens in practice as a result, and some help with defending yourselves against it.

If you need a straightforward digest of the rules and cases about supervision you can find it elsewhere. Modesty forbids me to tell you the best place to look.

When the law becomes crucially involved in construction supervision, there is already a loser: someone has suffered injury or damage to his person, property or pocket. It should not be surprising if he seeks the sympathy of the law and the law gives it to him - that merely reflects values that we all accept to one degree or another when we ourselves are losers. It seems to me to be unrealistic to believe that that the workman who has lost a leg on a construction site or the small businessman

Supervision of Construction. Thomas Telford Ltd, London, 1985

1

whose new factory has fallen down can be persuaded nowadays to refrain from using the courts on the grounds that it is morally better to suffer his loss in silence. Yet those who preach that the solution to the legal problems of supervisors and constructors is a return to times of stronger moral fibre, away from what is called 'consumerism', seem to believe that he can. The real problems are practical.

Questions: A supervisor (whether Engineer, contractor's agent, resident engineer or lesser mortal) alighting from his car on to a site on a grey morning, should be comforted if he knows the answers to the following practical questions:

1. (a) What are my legal functions and responsibilities ?

   (b) Consequently, what should I and should I not concern myself with on the site ?

2. (a) To what standards must I perform those functions and responsibilities ?

   (b) In particular, must I demand perfection from myself and others, or am I entitled to take practicality and money into account ?

3. (a) What consequences will happen to me, my family and employer if I do not meet that legal standard or meet it in the wrong way ?

   (b) Have I done everything possible so far, and do I know what to do in future, to reduce unpleasant consequences ? bluntly:

   A. What do I look for and what should I try not to see ?

   B. When I do see something wrong what should and can I do that does not cost too much for my 'side'.

   C. How can I keep the lawyers off my back, get on with my engineering and sleep peacefully at night ?

<u>Background Laws</u>: I have to start this far back,
because practicalities of law can be misconceived
disasterously if the sub-structure on which they
rest is ignored.

The basic commandment of all legal systems
is that supervision must not be negligent.   Our
law of negligence can be summarised shortly:

> "The liability for negligence ... is no
> doubt based upon a general public
> sentiment of moral wrongdoing for which
> the offender must pay ...   The rule
> that you are to love your neighbour
> becomes in law, you must not injure your
> neighbour: ... Who, then, in law is my
> neighbour ?   The answer seems to be –
> persons who are so closely and directly
> affected by my act that I ought
> reasonably to have them in contemplation
> as being so affected when I am directing
> my mind to the acts or omissions which
> are called in question."   (Donoghue v
> Stevenson [1932] A.C. 562,582).

> Our legal neighbourhood is becoming
> crowded.   It now includes not only all
> those who have a contract with us, or
> our employers, and so pay us directly or
> indirectly, but a multitude who do not.
> The tortious duty not to be negligent
> (independent of any contractual
> agreement to take care) is owed to
> workmen and members of the public who
> may be injured or have their property
> damaged by the works, or whose income
> may be reduced – all the way to a remote
> factory owner whose electrical power is
> cut off by the works, for example, and
> whom he may not know from Adam until he
> sues.   The duty also extends to
> negligent information – so that a
> supervisor may be liable to a contractor
> if he certifies to little for a progress
> payment in the negligent belief that
> some work is defective and should not be
> included.

> Negligence or not is a question of fact.
> To amount to negligence it must
> generally be proved that the course
> taken was one which no supervisor of

ordinary skill would have taken if he had been acting with ordinary care.

But if a supervisor holds himself out as a specialist he must have the ordinary skill of those who specialise in the particular branch. The crucial point is the skill he expressly or impliedly holds himself out as having, so that he may be liable if he takes on work which is beyond his capacity:

> Architects supervising erection of a building issued certificates to a contractor of completion of electrical plant installation. The employer paid on the certificates. The installation was eventually discovered to be defective and useless. The fault could only have been discovered by an expert in that type of plant.

> Held: That the architects were under a duty to satisfy themselves that the installation was satisfactory before issuing certificates, either by special knowledge or by the report of an expert, and were liable to pay the employer damages for failing to do so (Philip & Leslie v Transvaal Gold Fields Ltd. (1898) S.O.R. S45 Af.).

The burden is on the complainant to prove negligence, but the failure of an ordinary engineering job is evidence of negligence. Failure of a new method in which the supervisor did not profess experience is not.

Failing to obey professional rules or practice where there is a usual or normal practice is evidence of negligence.

It is normally a defence that the supervisor followed the practice of the majority of his profession or business, and the more technical the subject matter the more a court is forced to rely on the evidence of his fellow 'experts'. But in exceptional cases the general practice may itself be negligent, and a member will pay for his profession's sin.

The supervisor is under a duty to have and use a reasonable working knowledge of the law relating to his job, e.g. to comply with statutes and bye-laws; to acquaint himself within a reasonable time of major changes in the law by legislation or decisions of the courts.

Failure to read one article in the journals might not, but failure to be aware of a series of warnings about particular materials or a method of construction would generally be negligence.

Unhappily that neat summary suffers from the small defect that it does not altogether represent reality. For several reasons, including sympathy for the plaintiff and the fact that the judges have the luxury of time and hindsight in evaluating a decision made by a supervisor when he had neither (an example follows shortly), there is some tendency to apply a stricter standard in practice than in theory. In that way the professional man suffers not only in his pocket but also in his reputation, since the title 'negligence' is retained, with its implications of moral blame. It is true that Lord Denning, retreated when he saw where the charge for the plaintiffs in which he was in the vanguard was leading:

"In the second sentence the judge required Mr. Jordan to come up to 'the very high standard of professional competence that the law requires'. That suggests that the law makes no allowance for errors of judgment. This would be a mistake. Else there would be a danger, in all cases of professional men, of their being made liable whenever something happens to go wrong. Whenever I give a judgment, and it is afterwards reversed by the House of Lords, is it to be said that I was negligent ? Every one of us every day

5

> gives a judgment which is afterwards found to be wrong. It may be an error of judgment but it is not negligent. If they (medical men) are to be found liable whenever they do not affect a cure, or whenever anything untoward happens, it would do a great disservice to the profession itself. Not only to the profession but to society at large. Take heed of what has happened in the United States. ... We must say, and say firmly, that, in a professional man, an error of judgment is not negligent. To test it, I would suggest that you ask the average competent and careful practitioner: 'Is this the sort of mistake that you yourself might have made ?' If he says 'Yes, even doing the best I could, it might have happened to me', then it is not negligent." (Whitehouse v Jordan [1980] 1 All E.R. 650, 658).

For his pains, the learned judge was upbraided by purists, on the grounds that an error of judgment may be negligent -it depends how bad it is. The following recent dicta may be more typical of the judicial attitude:

> "The plaintiff's action sounds in negligence. This is an unfortunate name for the cause of action in this case because her complaint is not that the surgeons did something careless, such as leaving a swab in at an operation site, but rather that their considered decision showed a want of proper professional skill and care.
>
> The John Radcliffe Hospital and Professor Turnbull (the Defendant) are of the highest standing in their profession but I must not let that deter me from an examination of whether they proceeded with due professional care in the present case. Counsel ... referred to Professor Turnbull's status as 'Olympian'. My recollection of classical mythology is that the gods were no strangers to error.
>
> ...

I cannot leave this case without expressing my regret that I have had to spend so long examining the decision of so distinguished a gynaecologist as Professor Turnbull. I trust that what I have had to say in no way tarnishes a great reputation, and I would echo the words (of) Donaldson LJ.: "There are very few professional men who will assert that they have never fallen below the high standards rightly expected of them. That they have never been negligent. If they do, it is unlikely that they should be believed. And this is as true of lawyers as of medical men. If the judge's conclusion is right, what distinguishes Mr. Jordan from his professional colleagues is not that on one isolated occasion his acknowledged skill partially deserted him, but that damage resulted. Whether or not damage results from a negligent act is almost always a matter of chance and it ill becomes anyone to adopt an attitude of superiority".

Counsel for the defendants has referred to Professor Turnbull's Olympian reputation. I hope Professor Turnbull will take comfort in the thought that even Apollo, the god of healing, and the father of Aesculapius, had his moments of weakness".
(Clarke v McLellan [1983] 1 All E.R. 413,422,433 per Peter Pain J)

I fear that engineers must expect less of the normal judicial humility than is afforded to the medical profession (was there a god of engineering at all ?).

Those of you who work abroad will meet some legal systems, Nigeria, India and Pakistan are examples, that are based on exported English law, including the law of negligence. But it is wise to allow for differences in national temperament and organisation that may make the law in practice very different to the law on paper. If you do work in the United States multiply by three the problems mentioned in this paper.

You will also meet the 'civil law' systems, based on codes of law, throughout most of the Middle East, South America, and part of Africa and Asia. It is interesting that although they started out from a quite different direction, they have all reached something that in theory is like our law of negligence. But do not be mislead: because of their different procedures their allocation of blame for an identical failure or collapse may be diametrically different to ours.

And everywhere the law of negligence is developing - in some respects becoming more adventureous and in others retreating conservatively. For a supervisor to know his duties and rights he must not only know where the law is but plot where it is likely to move to in future. Refer below.

Conditions of Contract: A superstructure of standard terms of contract rises on those differentially settling foundations, notably the relevant clauses of the ICE and of the FIDIC International Conditions:

A. Clause 2 of both forms deals with the administration of supervision on behalf of the Engineer in language that is, to use a legal phrase, not suitable for the purpose for which it is intended. However, supervisors should carefully decipher the legal jargon, and write the letters that the clause requires so that the division of functions between supervisors will be organised in a sensible way in sensible language. I am involved in a case at the moment where a dispute about whether a particular power was or was not validly delegated by the Engineer to his representative has been considered by an arbitrator and four judges, and is not finished yet.

B. By clause 8(2) "... full responsibility for the adequacy, stability and safety of all siteoperations and methods of construction" is allotted to the contractor, and responsibility "for the design or specification of the Permanent Works (except as may be expressly provided in the Contract) or of any Temporary Works designed by the Engineer" is allotted to the Engineer. (Those quotes are from the ICE Conditions, the words in FIDIC are slightly different). If only it were that simple. Unfortunately that division never applies exclusively, but only concurrently with general law; clause 8(2) has no full power over anyone except the Employer and the Contractor (and through him sub-contractors) because only they are parties to and governed by the contract which gives the clause legal force, yet others can sue for negligence (above); anyway the division is limited and confused by later clauses.

C. The limitation and confusion starts with clause 13:

> (1) "Save in so far as it is legally or physically impossible the Contractor shall construct complete and maintain the Works in strict accordance with the Contract to the satisfaction of the Engineer and shall comply with and adhere strictly to the Engineer's instructions and directions on any matter connected therewith (whether mentioned in the Contract or not)"

(Incidentially, this sub-clause has been into the courts at least twice - most recently in NCB v Neill & Son [1984] All E.R. 555).

> "(2) The whole of the materials plant and labour to be provided by the Contractor under Clause 8 and the mode manner and speed of construction and maintenance of the Works are to be of a kind and conducted in a manner approved by the Engineer."

Add the definition in clause 1 that "Works" include temporary works.

D. I have expatiated elsewhere on the unique sub-clauses 13(3) and 14(3) - (6) of the ICE Conditions, and do not want to repeat myself, particularly as I have to admit that the chaos I predicted they would cause has not materialised. (I would add churlishly that it was the resilience of the industry and not the drafting of the clauses I underrated). Briefly, what they do is to put a price for the owner on some of the weapons of control in the Engineer's armoury that otherwise would be paid by the contractor, unless the Engineer manoeuvres so as to avoid using them and instead exercises control by the above quoted sub-clause 13(2).

9

E.   Finally, there is the variation clause 51 by which the Engineer is told that he "shall" (without any option) order any necessary variation to, in effect, the permanent or temporary works, which is then valued under clause 52.

(The references to "opinion of the Engineer" and similar phrases suggesting that he has the last word, should not give the Engineer delusions of grandeur.   By the Disputes clause 66/67 the arbitrator has "... full power to open up review and revise any decision opinion instruction direction certificate or valuation of the Engineer", including a decision not to give an instruction, direction or order).

Answers - General: It is part of the duty of the above legal sub-structure and superstructure to provide definite answers to the kind of question our supervisor asked at the beginning of this paper, so as to help projects to go right as well as distribute blame for those that go wrong. I am sorry to have to bear the news (if it is news to many of you) that, with fair help from the construction industry, they succeed in evading that duty very well.

Take a common case.   On a site inspection of the permanent works the Engineer sees that the contractor is using temporary works that are out of the ordinary, either in design or construction.   The first decision he has to make is whether to take comfort in clause 8 of the Conditions, ignore them and pass on, or is it his duty to get involved ?   That inescapable question opens a can of worms of several species, some legal, some engineering and some moral.

As often, a lawyer answers the question with a question - duty to whom ?   As we have seen, a supervisor has different and often conflicting duties to different people.   ·His own industry is doing much to make it difficult for him to know how to balance those duties.

We all like to refer to teams and teamwork, and the owner tends to believe the story that his project is in the hands of a united and devoted team of experts (unless he has been educated by experience, and until they start fighting amongst themselves). The trouble about that piece of salemanship by the industry is that the concept of a team involves joint responsibility amongst all the members for winning or losing.

If that is not what is really intended, but instead responsibility for design and contruction is intended to be parcelled out between several independent experts, each with liability only for his own limited part of the result, then the industry might be advised to make that clear and to define the parcels clearly.

The task is for the industry because, as the summary of the law shows, a judge does not take his decision on negligence or not out of the air: it depends on what function the accused undertook to perform. It is, of course, usage of the industry that largely decides what is the function of each member of the construction group (to use a neutral word).

If the industry, and its experts who speak for it on one side or the other in litigation, do no know what that usage is or only know that it is confused and uncertain, they cannot object that members are used as guinea pigs in the courts, and nor are they entitled to the satisfaction of complaining that the judges get it wrong when they themselves do not know what is right.

The perfect illustration is Oldschool v Gleeson: (1976) 4BLR 103:

> Contractors were sued for compensation by neighbours of the building site because a party wall collapsed as a result of failure of clay beneath foundations. They had excavated a hoist pit below the level of the party wall without taking proper precautions to support the foundations.

> The contractors proceeded to join the consulting engineers of the project owner into the proceedings, claiming reimbursement from them of the compensation paid to the neighbour, on the grounds that the accident was due to their negligence in supervision.

11

The case was held before the Official Referee.

In one corner - the partner in the firm of consulting engineers concerned (described by the judge as a Fellow of the Institute of Structural Engineers, a visiting lecturer on special structures at Leeds University and a winner of awards, with very considerable practical experience), with the Chief Engineer in the London office of one of the largest firms of consulting engineers acting as his second and expert witness.

In the other corner Mr. H, an extremely well know consulting engineer with exceptional experience as an expert witness, who was called to give evidence on behalf of the contractor.

The judge's analysis of events leading to the collapse fills 24 pages of the law report. It is based on the evidence of the experts and recollections of witnesses of fact under examination in chief, cross-examination and reexamination as to what happened 4 years before they gave their evidence, and some written records (including entries in a foreman's diary that the learned judge found "unsatisfactory, in the sense that they do not record warnings or complaints, when as I believe, these were given ... (which) leads me to think that he (the foreman) was not anxious to record criticism or complaints when they were made"). All with the benefit of hindsight.

The judge had to decide between conflicting evidence of the two main experts not only on the reason for sheer failure to the excavation, but also on the proper function of the consulting engineer, which he did in these words - "Plainly it is the consulting engineer's duty to produce a suitable design for the works which will achieve what the building owner requires, and it is further his duty to ensure that that design is carried out. The difference

of opinion between the experts - Mr.
H.... on behalf of the first defendants
and Mr. M... on behalf of the second
defendants - is as to the extent of the
consulting engineer's duty in regard to
the manner in which the contractors
execute the work in order to achieve the
required result. Here may I pay
tribute to the two experts, both of whom
are consulting engineers of high
qualification and considerable
experience and both of whom in my
estimation gave their evidence in
support of their respective opinions in
a manner deserving of the highest
praise. Mr. H... obviously is, if
he will forgive me saying so, of the
older school. Although he was disposed
to agree at one stage that a consulting
engineer's duty was to design and see
that the design was properly carried
out, but otherwise to leave the
contractors to get on with the job and
not give instructions as to how the work
was to be done, he nevertheless
maintained that it was still the
consulting engineer's duty to see that
the contractors executed the work in a
competent manner, particularly where the
safety of the works was involved. He
regards the consulting engineer as what
he described as being "the father and
mother of the job", whose duty it is to
direct the contractors as to the manner
in which the work is to be done, if he
sees that the method which they are
employing might endanger the safety of
the works, and to stop the work if
necessary. He considers it to be the
consulting engineer's duty to ensure
that the contractors carry out the work
in a manner which will not endanger the
safety of the works and thereby to
assume responsibility for insisting that
the contractors should undertake the
work, if necessary, in a manner and
sequence different from that which they
may have planned or may be proposing to
follow. Mr. M... on the other hand,
was equally insistent that the manner of
execution of the works is a matter for
the contractors. He considers that the
consulting engineer is in no position,

13

for instance, to require the contractors to comply with any particular sequence of works; he has no right let alone duty, to involve himself in the work of the contractors. Of course he would interest himself in their work, would offer advice to assist the job to go better and would certainly not turn his back on a situation that he could see was likely to give rise to danger to life. Equally he would intervene if he could see imminent damage to property. Those are matters of common sense; but that is a very different matter from assuming responsibility for the method of work to be adopted by the contractors. In my judgement, Mr. M's view is the right one".

After a few more pages the Referee then held up the consulting Engineer's arm as the winner.

9 lawyers and a judge were involved in the case, in a hearing that probably lasted about 10 days.

It is necessary to add to the law landscape one more large object, placed there by Parliament since that decision and facilitating the type of claim tried on in it. By the Civil Liability(Contribution) Act 1978, Parliament cooked-up what I have called Irish stew litigation, in which a claimant is facilitated in stirring together in legal proceedings as many defendants as he can find, in the hope of find at least one that is rich or insured.

The Act works in this way. A contractor constructs faulty sub-base over ten miles of road. The RE and the Engineer do not notice until the road is nearly finished. The contractor claims that if the Employer's supervisors had done their job properly his mistake would have been found when it would have been much less expensive to put it right. Under our system that is no defence to the contractor vis-a-vis the Employer. Neither has the contractor any direct claim against the Engineer or RE because they have no duty to him; their function is to protect the interests of the

Employer and not to protect the contractor against his own mistakes. Nevertheless, they are liable to the Employer because they did have a duty to him to discover the faulty work as soon as reasonably possible.

The Employer may sue all or any of the parties who are liable to him. In practice he will now usually sue everyone in sight, or if he choses to sue eg. only the contractor, the contractor will be entitled himself to join the Engineer and RE as co-defendants. The court will give the Employer judgment against each of the defendants who is liable (of course on the basis that he only recovers his compensation once). The court will also decide in what shares the defendant should bear the compensation (and the cost of the action) between themselves. If anyone pays more than his share to the Employer he is entitled to recover the excess from the others. So by a circuitous route, and despite the fact that they had no legal duty to him, the contractor is likely to succeed in getting back at the Engineer or RE for whatever share of the losses the judge considers "just and equitable having regard to th extent of (his) responsibility".

The picture is completed if I point out that the Act not only applies between two parties who both have a contract with the injured third party, but even those who do not have a contract with him but are liable for negligence in tort. The Employer or one of the original defendants might add into proceedings a site investigation firm employed by the Engineer or sub-contractors, with whom the Employer of course has no contract. An Employer in a case now current in Hong Kong is marinating 16 defendants.

Two special pitfalls in the Act. It is a consequence of the mechanism that if any of the defendants is insolvent and cannot pay his share of the compensation, the solvent ones have to pay for him. If the Engineer and contractor are held liable to contribute by the court in the respective proportions 5% and 95% of the damages but the contractor is insolvent, then the unfortunate Engineer has to pay all.

A very practical pitfall in multi-party proceedings is that even if all the defendants are solvent one who has been joined because he has a very subsidiary involvement, with at most the danger of a 5% contribution, will have to employ a full team of lawyers throughout the whole proceedings. Lawyers charge the same modest rate for both standing and working time. I believe there has been a recent example in the official Referee's court where the proportions were one lawyer working to twenty-one standing in the queue to examine some witness, with all their meter's ticking at the full rate.

The reverse side of the coin is the position of the contractor where defective design of the permanent works by the Engineer results in injury, damage or loss. Obviously the contractor will strongly claim exoneration under clause 8(1). But as before an injured workman or a neighbour on whose house the works have fallen, will answer that he knows nothing of the ICE Conditions; never bound himself to their terms by any contract with the contractor; and is claiming against the contractor in tort under the general law and not under any contract. We return to the point that the test is not based on the words of a particular contract as such, but on the proper function of a contractor in this type of construction. To refer back to my first quotation from the judges, in Donoghue v Stephenson on page 3, the contractor will argue that he was not properly involved in "directing (his) mind to the acts or omissions which are called in question", because those acts and omissions were the preparation of the permanent design which was not part of his function.

That argument will be stronger where the claim is made against the contractor by the Employer, who did agree to the terms of clause 8(2). When I was first involved in construction law I advised with youthful confidence that a contractor is perfectly entitled to construct works which he knew would fall down the day after practical completion because of some defect in the permanent design, and nevertheless would have performed his contract and be entitled to his money from the Employer. I was in good company in giving that advice, but I would not repeat it now.

I think a fair summary of the direction the law is taking not only in the UK but in the civil law systems, is to further confuse functions by holding that because the contractor is an expert in construction, he has a duty to warn whenever he becomes aware of a defect in the Engineer's design or, probably, should have become so aware as a reasonably competent and skilled contractor.

It is that last addition, if it is or becomes part of the law, that creates the largest problem. It begs the question of the extent to which a reasonable contractor will go out of his way to review the permanent design more than is necessary for the purpose of building what he has been told to build.

A contractor who keeps trying to tell consulting engineers their business may not stay long in his own.

While a major contractor will perform a public service by ensuring that any knowledge gained by one division of his organisation about a new type of failure is recorded and disseminated, he may by such service make a rod for his own back as a result of increasing the level of his company's knowledge on which a claimant may rely (having found out about it on an order for Discovery of documents) if the system for some reason does fail to avoid a similar failure in a particular case.

"How long O Lord how long" (Psalms 94.3.): It may be that when he contemplates the law in action as outlined so far, like a drowning man a supervisor's past misdeeds may flash through his mind. I should end these general comments by considering how much of his sinful past he should worry about.

The saga is well known of the efforts by the judges to make up their minds about how long liability for negligence lasts. Originally it was thought to last in most cases only for 6 years from the date when the negligence was committed: then lower courts changed their minds and appeared to make liability unlimited in time: then the House of Lords delivered itself of the last words in Pirelli v Oscar Faber [1983] 1 All E.R. 65).

The problem is the words they chose:

> The Plaintiff's cause of action ...
> accrues (when) damage occurs, which will
> commonly consist of cracks coming into
> existence as a result of the defect even
> though the cracks or the defect may be
> undiscovered and undiscoverable".

Some questions have been asked about that definition - what width does a crack have to attain before it represents "damage" ? Do tension cracks in concrete structures fall within the term "damage" if they in themselves are harmless but in the end they lead to corrosion of the steel reinforcement ?

> "There may perhaps be cases where the
> defect is so gross that the building is
> doomed from the start, and where the
> owner's course of action will accrue as
> soon as it is built" (before any
> "damage" has occurred).

You will note the precision and clarity of language, and understanding of construction and design philosophy exhibited in those quotations, and the degree of certain guidance they provide for those who must arrange their affairs (and insurance) in accordance with the decision.

And the saga has longer to run. Legislation is promised. In the meantime the House of Lords itself produced another episode a few weeks after the Perelli decision by giving judgment for an Employer in an action directly against a sub-contractor for the money that would have to be spent in replacing a floor laid negligently. No damage had yet occurred to the floor so that the House was enforcing a right of action which according to its previous decision did not yet exist.

Answers - Specific: In the absence of any excuse for delaying longer an attempt at some practical answers to practical questions:-

1. A supervisor should put on record that he has considered his responsibilites fully. He is more likely to be held guilty of negligence if he can be shown to have completely overlooked or

neglected his responsibilities, than if he only made an error of judgment in trying to fulfil them. The necessary consideration may be shown eg. by including (specifically minimum) requirements in the contract documents for protection of neighbouring property, and by diaries (see above) and other site records (a topic I do recall mentioning occasionally before). Preferably the supervisor should have a general system that will automatically establish his position.

2. I think that it is helpful in the present state of the law to divide duties into primary and secondary, based on the degree of control. The Engineer and his staff have primary responsibility, because they have primary control, for the design of the permanent works, but secondary responsibility for design and construction of temporary works. The reverse applies to the contractor. Construction of the permanent works appears to me to be an intermediate case, but with the greater degree of responsibility on the contractor. The Engineer has a positive duty to inspect permanent work, but not to be everywhere on the job all the time (even with an R.E.). Refer to the very detailed discussion of the Engineers' 'random' supervision in Florida Holidays v Mayo [1965] 113 CLR 588 Aust., and other cases that can be found in the books.

3. A supervisor should acquaint himself with the exact dividing line between primary and secondary responsibilities, and perhaps his professional or trade bodies may now or in the future be able to help to do so, and give him confidence that the division will be supported if necessary by evidence to a court of the trade usage.

4. Since secondary liability largely depends on knowledge, because there is no positive duty to find out, a supervisor should not be a busybody unless he is prepared and knows how to fulfil the larger responsibility he will be taking on.

5. A supervisor must have a system for acting on whatever knowledge he does obtain about his secondary and, of course, his primary, responsibilities. He must reconcile himself

to the fact that a duty to notify of risks is discharged only by a notification that is as effective as possible -

> "An Engineer employed by an Architect accepted the Architect's refusal to accept his recommendation that deep soil tests should be carried out. The Architect said that the client would not approve the cost. Held the Engineer owed a duty to inform the client directly; his warning to the Architect was not enough (District of Surrey v Church [1977] 76 D.L.R. (3d) 721 Can).

6. A supervisor will not be satisfied to know the test the courts say they are applying in divining negligence, but will keep up with the reports that show what the courts are actually doing in practice from time to time, and will reconcile his conduct to that reality.

7. The big problem is practicality, which usually means money:

(a) The Engineer may have a duty to his client, and to himself since the client is likely to sue him for the extra cost if he does not, to use the control mechanism at the cost of the contractor. There is very little, if any, difference in the effective power the Engineer has to take action on the grounds that the contractor is acting in a way that he has been told is not approved (and which normally cannot cost the Employer any money), and where he issues a positive instruction (for which the Employer may have to pay). Questions of professional good practice and the Engineer's general duty of independence and impartiality may come into play in determining how far the Engineer should manoeuvre to avoid paying the contractor compensation in cases where he has genuinely been caused unforeseen expense of a kind that the Conditions (despite their inconsistences) do clearly intend him to recover.

I do have a fear that a court might hold in favour of an injured third party that the Engineer is under a duty to intervene in the most positive way, that is by an instruction, even to suspend the works, in the case of danger.

(b)   If   a   risk   to others is being run because someone will   not   spend the money to avoid it, make sure he does not pass the buck to you but is well identified in the records.

(c)   If you are placing risks on others to save your   money,   whether   directly,   or   indirectly because you think your practice or business will suffer if you are intransigent with a good customer - prepare for judgment in this world and the next.

2   The JCT and GC Works Conditions of Contract

N. ROYCE, FRIBA, PPIArb, Practising architect and arbitrator

SYNOPSIS: In standard forms of contract in the construction industry, the responsibility for supervision falls between both the professional advisers and the contractor. The professional advisers, however, have a responsibility both in their advice to clients and in the preparation of the contract documents followed by their supervisory role during the course of the works through to completion. The main contractors responsibility of supervision not only involves his own works but those of the sub-contractors and is conditioned by his planning sequencing of the contract.

INTRODUCTION:

The JCT Form

1. Standard Forms of Building Contract are not a modern innovation. Most of us remember the 1963 Edition of the JCT (known as the RIBA Form), some the 1939 Edition, few of us the 1931 Edition, and they even date back to 1909 and before that there were certainly Standard Forms but not in popular usage as they are today.

2. Before 1947 there were only two participants in the work of evolving the Standard Form: the RIBA and the NFBTE. In 1947 they were joined by the RICS. Now the JCT is comprised of many constituent bodies.

3. In 1963 when the Joint Contracts Tribunal revised its terms of reference and admitted into membership FASS and CASEC, it was agreed that the Tribunal would prepare nominated sub-contract conditions and a standard tender for use with sub-contractors nominated by the Architect under the Standard Forms.

4. The package relating to nominated sub-contracts has been prepared from all the experience acquired with nomination over a period of years, and with due regard to the court decisions which have been made since the 1963 Edition was published.

5. The new NSC procedures recognise that many problems can be solved by resolving all details at the tender stage instead of leaving them to become the subject of expensive dispute at the contract stage.

6.   The new NSC procedures may initially appear cumbersome. They impose necessary disciplines, which have in the past been expensively disregarded.   They involve the use of an employer/nominated sub-contractor form of agreement (warranty agreement NSC/2).

The Standard Form of Building Contract

7.   This is the main document produced by the tribunal and is intended to be suitable for use on the majority of building contracts of medium to large size where the work has been designed in detail before the contract is entered into.   It is produced in three basic versions: (a) with firm quantities; (b) with approximate quantities; and (c) without quantities.

SUPERVISION UNDER JCT FORMS

Responsibility of the Architect/Supervising Officer under the JCT Form

8.   The architect should advise on the selection and appointment of the contractor and shall make such periodic visits to the site as he considers necessary to inspect generally the progress and quality of the work and to determine in general if the work is proceeding in accordance with the contract documents.

9.   The architect is not responsible for the contractor's operational methods, techniques, sequences or procedures, nor for safety precautions in connection with the work, nor shall he be responsible for any failure by the contractor to carry out and complete the work in accordance with the terms of the building contract between the client and the contractor.

10.   During his on-site inspections, the architect should endeavour to guard the client against defects and deficiencies in the work of the contractor, but should not be required to make exhaustive or continuous inspections to check the quality or quantity of the work.

11.   Where frequent or constant inspection is required a clerk or clerks of works should be employed.   He shall be nominated or approved by the architect and be under the architect's direction and control.   He may be appointed and paid by the client or employed by the architect.

12.   Where the need for frequent or constant on-site inspection by the architect is agreed to be necessary, a resident architect should be appointed by the architect.

GENERAL CONDITIONS OF GOVERNMENT CONTRACTS FOR BUILDING AND CIVIL ENGINEERING WORKS

Form GC Works/1

13.   This form is in general use in government departments and among some government corporations and the like; in these latter cases it may appear under some other title and may

have small differences in its contents. It is not suitable for adaptation for use by other public bodies or in the private sector.

Background to the Form

14. The form originates in an interdepartmental committee representing all ministries concerned with construction; this body consults with the major employers' federations in the construction industry in producing amendments to the form. The main locus of responsibility is now in the Property Services Agency of the Department of the Environment.

15. There are other related forms of mechanical and elect-rical direct contracts, for minor contracts and for sub-contracts. The first exists to meet the fairly frequent practice of placing direct contracts rather than nominated sub-contracts where engineering services are of high value in relation to the building work. It differs from the GC/Works/1 contract in many more respects than can be explain -ed by the difference in subject matter and has a number of unexpected omissions. The minor contracts form is suitable only for lump sums without quantities.

16. Some general points about the conditions contained in the form may be noted. One, which is evidenced by their title, is that they are intended both for building and for civil engineering work; they thus combine the purposes of the JCT form and the ICE form although the philosophy of their drafting is much more akin to that of the former. There are in fact none of the really distinctive features of the ICE form - and the conditions operate none the worse for that. Another feature is that they may be used with a variety of financial bases.

17. 'The Superintending Officer', abbreviated to 'the SO', takes the place of the architect under the JCT form. What is important is that he appears within the authority's organisation and not as an independent professional person standing between the parties. This is the contractual position even if outside consultants are engaged. The situation in which the authority will seek arbitration as a means of re-dress against the decision of the SO will therefore not arise.

18. The contract itself is evidenced by the tender on the one hand and a letter of acceptance on the other; there is no equivalent to the JCT articles of agreement. The form serving as invitation and form of tender also contains the abstract of particulars, which is the counterpart of the appendix to the JCT form. There can thus be no case of an English contract under seal and such a form in fact is not used by government departments.

19. While the conditions exhibit somewhat greater legal precision than the JCT form, and considerably more than the ICE form, they also include material which appears to be spelling out procedural points for the benefit of the SO or even perhaps of the authority. In practice 'the authority' may often be equated with the departmental contracts branch,

which in the governmental system of balance of power exists alongside the professional departments who in turn are en-shrined in the term 'the SO', except for the quantity surveyor and any resident engineer or clerk of works.

CLAUSES OF INTEREST

Firm Quantities

20. Conditions 5(1) and 5(2) run in a similar vein to the JCT with quantities form. The method of measurement is to be that expressed in the bills, rather than that any one standard method applies unless otherwise stated.

Provisional or Approximate Quantities

21. These two appear to be the same for practical purposes and are stated in condition 5(3) as though they are a variant form of quantities, so that the points about firm quantities will apply to them also. Once such quantities have been used for tendering, they become effectively a schedule of rates for remeasurement, as the condition implies.

Condition 7 - SL's Instructions

22. This condition is the equivalent of parts of JCT clause 4 in that it obliges the contractor to obey the SO's instructions. There is however no right for the contractor to obtain any substantiation of the SO's authority to order any matter in doubt. On the contrary, the SO's decision here is final and conclusive. The condition lists in one place the subject matter of the SO's instructions, whereas the JCT form considers such matters only under the various clauses concerned. It therefore covers variations, clarific-ations and a number of wide ranging issues, while further the list is open-ended since its last item begins 'Any other matter...' The specific inclusion of rights to instruct the contractor on the order of working, on hours of working, and on emergency action needed for security (whether of the works or the State is not defined), thus gives considerable scope to dictate matters which the JCT form leaves strictly to the contractor. The JCT form goes no further than allowing changes under clause 13.2 in obligations or restrictions already imposed by the employer in the contract. The SO is required to confirm in writing any oral instructions, but it is not made clear whether or not the instructions are valid and must be obeyed if they remain oral. Certainly the condition forbids the contractor making any variation without the SO's instructions. There is no provision for the contractor to confirm oral instructions back to the SO so that they become valid after a waiting period. The next condition might just help here.

Condition 8 - Failure of Contractor to Comply with SO's Instructions

23. This is equivalent to further parts of JCT clause 4, and like it allows other persons to be employed to carry

out work arising out of instructions that the contractor has not implemented after a written notice requiring compliance. Presumably if the contractor were to wait for such a notice before complying he could obtain written confirmation of a sort this way, if his earlier request had for some reason not been met. This is something of a counsel of desperation, only to be thought of in abnormal circumstances.

INSPECTIONS DURING CONSTRUCTION

Architect/Supervising Officer Duties in Site Inspections

24. When once the main contract for the construction of building works has been entered into the Architect/Supervising Officers primary duty to the building owner is concerned with the direction and supervision of the works to ensure that they are carried out to the standard dimensions, form and quality which the contract requires and with the furnishing of any further information which the contractor may require to enable the works to be completed within the contract time for completion within the contract sum.

25. It will be seen from the authority given to the architect by the building owner and the contractor under a contract in the JCT Forms that during the execution of the work he has sufficient powers necessary to ensure that his directiona nd supervision may be effective in regard to enforcing the contract requirements.
(Subject to Arbitration or the Courts)

26. But how far an architect is responsible to the building owner for detailed supervision and detailed tests of the works in progress, and how far he is relieved of responsibility by the employment of a clerk of works constantly engaged upon the works is not quite so clear. But that the building owner is entitled to expect that the architect will make sufficient visits to the works, and on those visits make a sufficient investigation of the methods and manner in which the work is being carried out to ensure that the works are being executed substantially in accordance with his drawings and specifications, is established, but constantly changing.

RIBA Conditions of Engagement

27. By clause 1.33 it is provided that the architect "shall make such periodic visits to the site as he considers necessary to inspect generally the progress and quality of the work and to determine in general if the work is proceeding in accordance with the contract documents".

28. By clause 1.60 "during his on-site inspections . . the architect shall endeavour to guard the client against defects and deficiencies in the work of the contractor, but shall not be required to make exhaustive or continuous inspections to check the quality or quantity of the work." Clause 1.61 provides for the appointment of a clerk of works "where frequent or constant inspection is required" and by

clause 1.62 for the appointment of a resident architect, each of whom is to be paid for by the client.

29. It is part of __an architect's duty__ to advise the client when a clerk of works and a resident architect should be appointed. Clause 1.34 provides that the architect shall not "be responsible for any failure by the contractor to carry out and complete the works in accordance with the terms of the building contract between the client and the contractor".

30. It is often urged on behalf of architects that their duty in regard to inspection is in some way limited to the making of a reasonable number of visits to the site during its execution, but in my opinion the number of visits is by no means a criterion by which the discharge of their duties will be tested. Everything will depend upon the stage of the work at the time of the visit and the opportunity which the visit gives them, to see the works in a state, that will enable the facts to be ascertained, on which the satisfactory execution of the works depend.

31. In the much quoted case of Leicster Guardians v Trollope as long ago as 1911, it was held that an architect was liable for dry rot which had broken out four years after the building had been completed, becuase he had failed to see that the floors had been constructed in a manner which ensured their ventilation and with the materials which had been specified. The judge said in that case:-

32. If the architect had taken steps to see that the first block was all right and had then told the clerk of works that the works in the others were to be carried out in the same way, I would have been inclined to hold that the architect had done his duty; but in fact he did nothing to see that the design was complied with. In my view this was not a matter of detail which could be left to the clerk of works.

Failure to Examine Site, Foundations Etc

33. An architect or engineer is liable to his employer for any damages resulting to the employer for any neglect to employ the usual and proper means for examining the site, soil and adjoining buildings both before during the construction period. If an architect is employed to design a building, he ought, in order to do so, to obtain authority from the building owner to examine the site of the proposed building and to ascertain the nature of the subsoil upon which the building is proposed to be built. He is also liable for failing to inspect the foundations at proper times, and often enough - during the progress of the works.

34. Where an architect is instructed to build on old foundations, or to raise an existing building he is liable to his employer for any neglect to test the walls or test the stability of the under-lying structures.

35. An architect is not bound to make a personal examination but if he does not make such examination and adopts incorrect information furnished by others, he is equally

liable.

36. This liability rests on the professional duty of the architect to examine and test, by his own professional knowledge, statements or plans made by others with reference to the work which he has undertaken.

37. It has been said that failure is not equivalent to negligence. What you have to do is to exercise reasonable care, not super-human care, or greater than average care and although things can go wrong which can indicate some lack of care it does not automatically lead to liability.

Issue of Final Certificates

38. Clause 30.8 states: So soon as is practicable but before the expiration of 3 months from the end of the Defects Liability Period stated in the Appendix or from completion of making good defects under clause 17 or from receipt by the Architect or by the Quantity Surveyor of the documents referred to in clause 30.6.1.1, whichever is the latest, the Architect shall issue the Final Certificate and inform each Nominated Sub-contractor of the date of its issue.

39. And Clause 30.9 states: (.1) Except as provided in clauses 30.9.2 and 30.9.3 (and save in respect of fraud), the Final Certificate shall have effect in any proceedings arising out of or in connection with this Contract (whether by arbitration under article 5 or otherwise) as (.1.1) conclusive evidence that where the quality of materials or the standard of workmanship are to be to the reasonable satisfaction of the Architect the same are to such satisfaction, and (.1.2) conclusive evidence that any necessary effect has been given to all the terms of this contract which require that an amount is to be added to or deducted from the Contract Sum or an adjustment is to be made of the contract sum save where there has been any accidental inclusion or exclusion of any work, materials, goods or figure in any computation or any arithmetical error in any computation, in which event the Final Certificate shall have effect as conclusive evidence as to all other computations.

40. This clause, by freeing the contractor from a liability for defects subsequently ascertained, makes the examination of the works during execution a matter of very high importance, and entitles the contractor, to take advantage of the failure of the architect to have made an examination which would disclose the defects. The fact that the contractor may be relieved of this liability throws a greater responsibility upon the architect, and a building owner who finds that the works have been defectively constructed, and he is without redress against the contractor, may properly seek his redress at the hands of the architect.

41. The employment of a clerk of works, constantly engaged upon the works, may relieve the responsibility of the architect for defective works, of a minor character,

as there must be an implication, that the architect is entitled to leave the detailed examination of the work, to such person, and will not be responsible for any failure on his part, to discover the defect, if, as is usual, he is employed by the building owner, and not by the architect. This immunity of the architect cannot, I suggest, be applied to defects of a radical character or to any feature of construction upon which the stability or the effectiveness of any important part of the building or trade employed depends. Moreover, once the attention of the architect has been drawn, either by the building owner himself, by the clerk of works, or by his own inspection to the execution of defective works by the contractor, it becomes his duty, to require the defective work to be remedied at once, and to give a closer attention in the future, to the inspection and testing of the works.

42. In such a case he is not justified in allowing the defective works to remain, for re-execution, until some future date, nor to assume that the defects are of an isolated character, and may not be repeated at a later date - particularly if the defects of which his attention is drawn indicate a deficiency in the work, which will result in less cost to the contractor, than if the work were carried out correctly. Similarly, if once the architect has found, or had his attention drawn, to defects which indicate that the inspection by the clerk of works is not reliable, he cannot any longer rely upon the employment of a clerk of works as an excuse for not making his own inspection of the work.

43. The powers of the architect in relation to requiring the contractor to remove defective materials or works, are exercisable during the construction of works, and are quite distinct from his powers to require the contractor to make good defects after the works have been substantially completed.

44. The building owner is entitled to expect that the architect will exercise these powers, at the time when the defect has been discovered, so that when the works are certified by the architect to be substantially complete, such defects will have been made good. An architect who neglects to give an order condemning works or materials which he has or ought to have seen to be defective, before giving a certificate which releases part of the retention money, may cause loss to the building owner and in consequence be held liable for his failure.

Quality Control

45. The building industry as a whole is judged by the quality of the finished building. The contractor is legally responsible for carrying out and completing the work in accordance with the contract documents to the reasonable satisfaction of the architect; the architect may be accountable to the employer if he passes for payment work which

30

is not satisfactory. Work of this quality will not be obtained without proper organisation (a) by the architect's ensuring that the drawings, specification, and other instructions indicate quite clearly what is required; and (b) by the contractor's creating conditions on site in which the work can be properly carried out. Thereafter, the contractor's site management must be responsible for ensuring that the standard of work, including that of sub-contractors, whether they are nominated or not, is in accordance with the contract and to the reasonable satisfaction of the architect. The contractor's responsibility for this is in no way diminished by the architect's duty to provide periodic supervision and inspection.

46. The architect and other consultants can assist by ensuring that the work specified, and their instructions, are capable of being properly interpreted; this may entail the erection of sample panels on site and the inspection of manufactured components at the factory. Work that is not in accordance with the contract should be condemned by site management at once: the longer sub-standard work remains, the more costly it is for the contractor to replace it. To delay giving such an instruction will inevitably affect the issue of the Certificate of Practical Completion, with resulting repercussions on the employer's programme for occupation, and the issue to the contractor of the final certificate.

Discussion on Papers 1 and 2

DR J. F. UFF (CHAIRMAN)

Mr Abrahamson: could you comment on the note in Mr
Fitzpatrick's paper that the duty of a contractor might
include warning of design defects? Secondly, are contractors
and engineers usually aware of the particular conditions of
contract under which they are working?

MR M. W. ABRAHAMSON

American, European and to some extent home authorities have
established or are pointing clearly in the direction of a duty
to warn - as referred to in my own paper. The cause,
obviously, is the belief of the courts that a project owner
(and the public) is entitled to the benefit of the skill of
all the experts engaged on a project, so they will not allow a
contractor who holds himself out as qualified in civil
engineering to disown responsibility to the owner or an
injured third party for a large element in the project which
is within the general area of his expertise.

On the second question, whatever may have been the case in
the past, contractors and engineers now are usually well aware
not only of the type but also of the details of the conditions
of contract.

DR J. F. UFF (CHAIRMAN)

Mr Sandberg: could you comment on the effect of the
uncertainty about how many parties might be held liable for a
particular loss?

MR A. SANDBERG, Senior Partner, Messrs Sandberg, London

My main concern is the increased liability which is falling on
those parties still in existence, the increase being due to
the defection of others either because of liquidation or

because private arrangements had been made with the client in
order that the case against them should be withdrawn.

DR J. F. UFF (CHAIRMAN)

Mr Griffiths: are insurers content with multiparty litigation
or are they prepared to countenance project insurance?

MR K. E. O. GRIFFITHS

Insurers have no choice in the litigation to which they are
exposed. It is an inevitable part of underwriting liability
insurances of any kind. If by project insurance you mean a
material damage insurance covering the interests of the owner,
designer and builder in the project works then there is a
market for such cover, and it is likely to reduce the amount
spent on litigation compared with the traditional approach.
Nevertheless it is a very expensive form of cover and the
risks covered are normally limited to collapse and imminent
collapse. The insurance market would certainly countenance
project insurance - the main reason it has not become popular
is that it costs much more than a more traditional approach.

MR G. M. HANNAH, Partner, Hannah, Reed & Associates, Cambridge

Under the ordinary ACE terms of appointment the Engineer has a
duty to 'make sufficient site visits to satisfy himself that
the general standards of construction are satisfactory'.
   It is therefore no excuse, as had been implied by a previous
speaker, to say since no site visits had been made that the
Engineer could not be liable for items overlooked on a site
visit. The Engineer is expected to make a number of visits
under his terms of appointment.

DR J. F. UFF (CHAIRMAN)

Mr Royce: does the fact that architects' supervision on
building projects is periodic affect the standard of
efficiency of inspection?

MR N. ROYCE

It is extremely difficult to maintain the efficiency of
inspections if only periodic inspections are made by an
architect. In practice it is customary for an architect to
make more frequent visits to a site during crucial periods
such as during foundation works, the co-ordination of services
in air-conditioning and during the laying of flat roofs and I

always recommend that a clerk of works be appointed in order that daily or even hourly inspections can be made during the course of complicated works.

Having said this, the architect always works closely with the Consulting Engineer and takes the advice of the Consulting Engineer in all matters beyond his expertise in the engineering field.

DR J. F. UFF (CHAIRMAN)

Mr Lee: what is the view of consultants on the imposition of fee competition?

MR D. J. LEE, Partner, G. Maunsell & Partners, London

There is a great danger in cost cutting leading to less supervision, and designs less well conceived and checked. There will be a settling-in period in the UK with many problems and heart searching. However, fee competition has been with us for many years in overseas practice and it is true that many overseas clients, including public and private, think that they can obtain a bargain by taking low tenders and doing some horse-trading. They have to learn by experience that this is not the way to find satisfaction. The long-suffering consultant should stick to the professional standards and clients will respect him for it in the long term.

On a positive note, it is important that price is not the starting point of a fee negotiation. Any lump sum looks too big to a client. It is much better to evolve a clear brief for the services required - is it two men or ten for six months' supervision, and what is the quality of experience? If these matters are set out as a schedule then the extension of men months to cost is made simpler. Within cost brackets an experienced engineer or technician plus overheads is not much different from one UK consultant to another. Hence it is what the consultant is going to do rather than his lump sum cost that is the primary factor. At the end of the day most clients want a good job and are prepared to pay for it. Professional fees are such a small percentage of the total cost of a project that it is absurd that fee competition should be made out to be a significant issue in reducing project costs.

DR J. F. UFF (CHAIRMAN)

Mr Deuce: why had the new ICE conditions for ground investigation continued to accept competitive tendering?

MR T. L. G. DEUCE

The conditions of contract are unrelated to the method or form
of tendering. They only come into force after the contract
has been entered into. However, it is worth pointing out that
had the conditions been able to influence the form of tender
my committee would not have sought to abandon competitive
tendering or to have made any other change which was not
necessitated by the dictates of ground investigation work.

MR D. F. JAMES, D. F. James & Partners, Ashford

I am perturbed at a situation that is prevalent these days
whereby should a party find itself as the minor defendant of
an action, should the parties be in liquidation or 'men of
straw', then the party could find itself as a main defendant
with sums of money awarded against it of a disproportionate
amount. Recently I have heard of a clerk of works who was
held liable to 20% of the damages mainly because other parties
were in liquidation. Should not equity prevail and the
contribution to the damages of the parties liable be
apportioned?
   At present it appears as though a professional person is not
only fully but also indefinitely responsible for his errors.
I am now defending an 82 year old person, who retired from
practice 17 years ago, against a claim for a recent defect in
a building built in 1965. Should there be a 'cut-off' period
against claims as there is in continental law?

MR J. WASILEWSKI, Associate, Harris & Sutherland, London

What is the difference between 'supervision' and 'inspection'
with particular reference to responsibility and liability
which follow?

MR N. ROYCE

Inspection means periodic examination of various aspects of
the work, which is not dissimilar to that of a building
inspector visiting the site. An architect carries out
periodic inspections to ensure that the works are being
executed in accordance with the terms of the Contract.
   It is often urged on behalf of architects that their duty
with regard to inspection is in some way limited to the making
of a reasonable number of visits to the site during its
execution, but in my opinion the number of visits is by no
means a criterion by which the discharge of their duties will
be tested. Everything will depend on the stage of the work at
the time of the visit and the opportunity which the visit
gives them to see the works in a state that will enable the

facts to be ascertained on which the satisfactory execution of the works depend.

Supervision implies a reasonable continuous inspection of works and, together with the responsibility of telling operatives how the work should be done, supervision is usually carried out by the main contractor in connection with both his domestic sub-contractors and the nominated sub-contractors.

In large contracts it is customary for a clerk of works to be employed to perform daily inspections and in many contracts a site architect is employed for a similar purpose.

MR R. FREER, Engineer, Pencol Engineering Consultants, London

Mr Chairman: you have invited the views of lawyers, contractors, consultants and insurers but not yet those of the clients. The client's view is often that he simply requires a satisfactory building within the estimated cost and within the estimated time and he is indifferent about how it is done. We make matters difficult for ourselves by using a system which is too complex and when we correct it we make it more complex so that, for instance, we produce a document which requires six months to read and understand but we allow the Contractor only six weeks to tender for the job.

We are all experts in different skills and I think that this should be recognized in the composition of the construction team in a practical manner. For instance before the work is started the responsibilities for each part of the work in that particular job should be defined and confirmation given to the client that those risks are insured against, perhaps using one insurance company for the complete construction team. I suggest that this would substantially reduce the avoidable volume of paperwork produced in the conditions of contract and the specification, which sometimes defeats its own objective by the shear bulk of paper.

The luxury of a high moral fibre exemplified by the Victorian contractors was based on their high profits. Brassey for instance often made 100% profit and he could afford to rebuild what failed at his own cost. Today the well-organized professional man has made sure that he is a financial man of straw: the house is in his wife's name and the capital is in trust for his children.

MR E. JAMES, Senior Lecturer, Hatfield Polytechnic

In this discussion we have been talking about being penny wise and pound foolish. I should like to give a further example of this, i.e. site investigation.

Site investigation contracts should not be awarded on the basis of competitive tendering. The average site investigation contract is about 2-4% of the total project cost (say 3%).

As far as the client is concerned, by having competitive tendering he is saving a mere 10% of the site investigation contract price, i.e. 0.3% of the total project cost. For this 0.3% 'saving' he could fail to obtain an adequate site investigation or even be given misleading information from the site investigation report which may only be discovered during the actual construction at great extra cost and time delay.

A site investigation contractor is more than a 'shell and auger man': he is a consultant as well and should be treated as such.

3 Standard conditions of engagement of consultants

T. W. WEDDELL, Head of Contracts, R. Travers Morgan and Partners, London

SYNOPSIS. Five different standard conditions of engagement are compared and their requirements relating to supervision are highlighted. The legal implications of these requirements are described by reference to legal judgments. Possible future changes are considered in the light of increased litigation and fee competition. These include limitation of liability, project insurance and the use of different systems for the execution of building and civil engineering projects.

INTRODUCTION

1. As the present system of carrying out building and civil engineering projects in the U.K. has developed, the terms of construction contracts have become standardised. Various standard forms of contract have been produced.

2. In the standard forms there invariably exists a person who is responsible for supervising the works. He is described as the Engineer, Architect or Superintending Officer (S.O.) etc. according to the particular form of contract. For convenience he will be referred to in this paper as the Supervisor although this term is not favoured by some. He is not a party to the construction contract, but fulfils a vital role in the contract.

3. The Supervisor has frequently been described as fulfilling two distinct functions, namely as agent of the Employer representing the Employer's interests, and also as an independent party acting fairly and impartially between the two contracting parties. (ref. 1)

4. Frequently the Supervisor is appointed from outside the Employer's organisation eg. a Consulting Engineer, an architect in private practice. He is normally, though not necessarily, the one appointed to design the works and prepare the contract documents.

5. In the same way that standard forms of construction contract developed, there have emerged standard forms of engagement acceptable to both Employer and Supervisor.

Basic Requirements of Standard Conditions of Engagement

6. The basic requirement of any contract of engagement is that it should be entirely consistent with the Supervisor's role in the construction contract – See Fig 1. It should define

Supervision of Construction. Thomas Telford Ltd, London, 1985

39

clearly the extent of the services to be provided, and make provision for any additional work or services which may be required. (ref. 2)

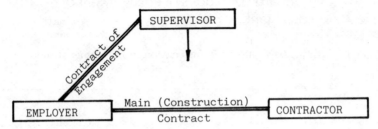

Fig. 1 Relation of parties to the Construction Contract and the Supervisor's Contract of Engagement.

7.   The minimum requirement is that the Supervisor should carry out his duties, and exercise his powers so that he properly fulfils his function in the construction contract. His contract of engagement should not fetter him in any way that interferes with his supervisory function. Any attempt to interfere with the Supervisor's authority expressed in the construction contract, whether by means of the terms of his contract with the Employer or otherwise, may result in his disqualification, which would be greatly against the Employer's interest.

8. Standard conditions of engagement, are often stated in general terms such that the Supervisor may operate under more than one of the standard forms for the main contract. For example, the Association of Consulting Engineers Conditions of Engagement 1981 Agreement 3, is suitable for use in Civil, Mechanical Electrical and Structural work each of which may be carried out under different forms of contract.

9.   Other matters such as technical and financial reporting and remuneration may be included though they may be of no concern to the Contractor.

SOME STANDARD CONDITIONS

ACE Conditions of Engagement 1981

10.   The Association of Consulting Engineers has published standard Conditions of Engagement for five different types of appointment. These Conditions together with the associated standard Memorandum of Agreement constitute the recommended standard form of Agreement in each case.

11.   The two standard agreements most relevant to the present discussion are:

Agreement 2. Conditions of Engagement for Civil Mechanical and Electrical Work and for Structural Engineering Work where an Architect is not appointed by the Client.

Agreement 3. Conditions of Engagement for Structural Engineering Work where an Architect is appointed by the Client.

Since the substance of these two agreements is similar, only Agreement 2 will be described and used for the purpose of comparison with the other standard conditions. It will be referred to as ACE2.

12. Clause 6 of ACE2 describes "Normal Services" and under the heading "Construction Stage" lists 12 matters, all or any of which may be necessary in a particular case. Clause 7 lists a number of "Additional Services".

13. Clause 8 "Supervision on Site" deals with appointment of site staff and Clause 10 states three alternative methods of payment for "Normal Services". Payment for site supervision is based on salary payments plus a percentage for head office overheads.

RIBA Architects appointment 1982

14. The Royal Institute of British Architects publication "Architects appointment", published in June 1982 referred to below as RIBA 82 comprises four parts. It includes a sample Memorandum of Agreement and Schedule of Services and Fees.

15. Part 1 lists services normally to be provided under 11 work stages, the last two of which are relevant to supervision of construction viz.

Work Stage K: Operations on site
Work Stage L: Completion
Part 2 "Other Services" lists provision of site staff and management.

16. Part 3 contains Conditions of Appointment and includes duty of care, responsibility of the Contractor, site inspection and site staff. Part 4 describes the recommended methods of calculating fees.

PSA/ACE Standard Conditions of Engagement for Civil Engineering, Structural Engineering and Public Health Engineering Commissions Interim Edition August 1983 (referred to as PASC (CE))

17. These standard conditions have been prepared by a Joint Working Party of the Property Services Agency and the Association of Consulting Engineers.

18. These conditions provide for the appointment of a consultant as part of a project management team which includes such parties as a Project Manager (a PSA Officer) a Lead Consultant, Associate Consultants, a Services Co-ordinator, a Superintending Officer and a Liaison Officer. The Consultants are required to follow the procedures outlined in the PSA publication "Consultant's Procedural Guide".

19. Condition 2 describes the four stages of a PSA project. Stage 3 deals with construction. "Normal duties", "Additional duties" and the Lead Consultant's duties are listed separately.

20. Condition 13 states that the Consulting Engineer will not, unless specifically commissioned, be responsible for the supervision of construction but only for those duties listed in Condition 4.

Department of Transport Model B Consultancy Agreement (referred to as DTpACE 81)

21. This standard agreement is used by the Department of Transport when engaging consulting engineers to design and supervise road and bridge schemes.

22. The Consultant's supervisory obligations are described in Clauses 10 and 11 under the heading "Progress of the Works Supervision". These include providing all necessary supervision

including inspection and testing, employing site staff,
reporting progress, financial control and contract reporting.
Other clauses state the Consultant's duty to measure the Works,
issue certificates, and give decisions on claims, accounts and
disputes.

23. Clause 16 defines the "Remuneration of Consultants".
This comprises a Basic Fee calculated on a percentage basis 30%
of which is in respect of supervision of construction.

The Landscape Institute Conditions of Engagement and
Professional Charges 1979 (referred to as LI79)

24. This document is used for the appointment of Landscape
Consultants on landscape works. It includes a number of clauses
of an explanatory nature. It empowers the Landscape Consultant
to "act as the agent of the client in the direction and
supervision of the work ...". The Landscape Consultant is
required to supervise the work by periodic inspections, but not
to make exhaustive or continuous inspection of the work. The
conditions however do provide for full time or part-time site
staff where frequent or constant inspection is required.

THE STANDARD FORMS COMPARED

25. The following comparison is limited to the five standard
forms described above, though others exist. Some bodies have
their own standard conditions which are frequently adapted from
one of the published standards. Of the five standard forms of
engagement described above, ACE2, RIBA82 and LI79 are unilateral
documents. The other two PASC(CE) and DTpACE 81 are the result
of agreements reached between PSA and DTp respectively and the
ACE.

Who should supervise?

26. ACE2 states that it is normal practice for the Consulting
Engineer who prepared the initial report to be appointed for
design and supervision. However the form also provides for a
party other than the designer to be appointed to supervise.
Similarly RIBA82 is sufficiently flexible to permit supervision
by a party other than the designer. Both DTpACE 81 and LI79
assume that supervision is by the designer. But there have been
recent instances of roads and bridges being supervised by
parties other than the designer. By contrast PASC(CE) states
that the Consulting Engineer will not, unless specifically
commissioned, be responsible for the supervision of construction
(Condition 13).

27. In USA, there is a strong body of opinion that
supervision of construction (sometimes called construction
review) must be carried out by the designer. E.B. Howell, the
President of Design Professionals Financial Corporation, has
stated that his company refuses to insure design professionals
who perform the construction review function on someone else's
plans and specification (ref. 3). He has cited various case
histories to demonstrate how failures could have been avoided if
the designers had supervised the construction.

The standard of care

28. The standard of the duty of care required of the
Consultant is described variously as the exercise of "reasonable

skill care and diligence" (ACE2, PASC(CE), DTpACE 81) and
"reasonable skill and care in conformity with the normal
standards of the architects profession" (RIBA 82). LI79 is
silent on the matter, but the gap is filled by statute. Section
13 of the Supply of Goods and Services Act 1982 states:
"In a contract for the supply of a service where the supplier is
acting in the course of a business there is an implied term that
the supplier will carry out the service with reasonable care and
skill".

29. Thus the Consultant in supervising construction of the
works does not assume absolute liability; he does not undertake
to guarantee or "ensure" that the Contractor's workmanship is
entirely in accordance with the contract, or that it is fit for
the purpose. Nor can he do so – that risk would be the
Contractor's. The Consultant's duty is the professional one (in
common with other professions) viz. the duty of exercising the
reasonable skill and care of the ordinary competent professional
man.

Services under the Main Contract

30. ACE2 includes "performing any services which the
Consulting Engineer may be required to carry out under any
contract for the execution of the Works" (Clause 6.3K). RIBA 82
includes the obligation to "administer the terms of the building
contract during operation on site" (Clause 1.21). DTpACE 81
states "The Consultants shall provide all supervision necessary
for them to fulfil the functions and duties of the Engineer to
the Contract" (Clause 10).

31. By contrast, the Consultant under PASC(CE) is not the
Superintending Officer under the main contract. The Consultants
obligations are limited to specific tasks such as commenting on
and advising, the S.O. on various matters (Condition 4).
The Landscape Consultants' services are described as follows:
"He will act as the agent of the client in the direction and
supervision of the work, and settle the financial account
between the client and the contractor, acting as arbitrator if
necessary in any area of dispute" (Condition 1.1). Notwithstanding the general requirement for the Consultant to perform
services required under the main construction contract, each
form also mentions specific obligations included in such
services thus producing some "double counting".

Appointment of Site Staff

32. Most of the standard conditions require the Supervisor
to supervise the Works in general terms, leaving the detailed
day to day checking and monitoring of material and workmanship,
to site staff.

33. ACE2 requires that the Client "shall agree" to the
appointment of such site staff as the Consulting Engineer shall
consider reasonably necessary. Site staff employed directly by
the Client, must first be selected and approved by the
Consulting Engineer. There are similar provisions in DTpACE 81
for the employment of a Resident Engineer and such other staff
as may be necessary.

34. RIBA82 includes a requirement to advise on the need for

site staff. Clause 2.37 of "Other Services" lists "provides
site staff for frequent or constant inspection of the works".
Provision is made in Clause 3.11 for the employment either by
the client or architect of a clerk of works where frequent or
constant inspection is required. Clause 3.12 provides for the
appointment of a resident architect on a part or full time basis.
L179 provides for the employment of a suitably qualified clerk
of works and/or resident landscape consultant when required.

35. One of the duties of the Lead Consultant under PASC(CE)
is to advise the Project Manager on appointment of resident site
staff (Condition 4 Duty 80). Condition 13 states that site
control staff may be provided by the PSA or Consulting Engineer.

36. The numbers and calibre of site staff are matters of
judgment in each case. Matters to be considered include the
complexity of construction, competence of the contractor, and
consequences of any defects which may occur (ref. 4).

Extent of Supervision

37. The detailed requirements in the standard conditions
regarding involvement of the Supervisor in supervision vary
considerably. ACE2 covers the point in some detail. It
requires the Consulting Engineer (Clause 6.36) to inspect and
test machinery and plant during manufacture and installation "as
are usually inspected and tested by Consulting Engineers". It
also requires the Consulting Engineer (Clause 6.3c) to advise
the Client on the need for special inspection or testing.

38. ACE2 also requires the Consulting Engineers to examine
the "Contractor's proposals" (Clause 6.3f). This is not
specific and presumably refers to such things as mode and manner
of execution of the Works (clause 13 ICE Conditions of Contract).

39. The Consulting Engineer is required to make "such visits
to site as he shall consider necessary to satisfy himself as to
the performance of any site staff appointed and so satisfy
himself that the Works are executed generally according to the
contract and otherwise in accordance with good engineering
practice" (Clause 6.3g).

40. DTpACE 81 requires the Consultant to provide all
supervision and direction necessary to fulfil the functions and
duties of the Engineer to the contract (Clause 10). This
includes inspection and testing of work and material and the
supervision of work procedures. The allocation of supervisory
duties between Consultant and site staff must depend to some
extent on the powers delegated to site staff (eg. under clause 2
ICE Conditions of Contract). However, DTpACE 81 refers to work
"which is proper to the Consultant's head office staff" and work
"which is proper to the Resident Engineer and his staff" (Clause
16c and d) suggesting that such allocation is based on custom.

41. RIBA 82 avoids use of the terms "supervise" and
"supervision" and states (Clause 3.10) that "The Architect will
visit the site at intervals appropriate to the stage of
construction to inspect the progress and quality of the works
and to determine that they are being executed generally in
accordance with the contract documents. The architect will not
be required to make frequent or constant inspections". Clause

44

3.9 states that the client will hold the contractor and not the architect responsible for the proper execution of the Works.

42. The question arises whether the architect can ever be liable for neglect of his inspecting duties under Clause 3.10, when Clause 3.9 appears to relieve him of liability for the proper execution of the work. The matter is further discussed below.

43. The only visits to site by the Consultant, under PASC(CE) are for the purpose of verifying design assumptions, attending site meetings when required to clarify Working Drawings and specifications, and to comment to S.O. on the adequacy of site supervision and quality control (Condition 4 Duty 55). His duties relating to inspection and testing are limited to agreeing the requisite procedures (Condition 4 Duty 50) rather than carrying out the inspections and testing himself, unless the latter is expressly instructed (Duties 62, 65). Also the S.O. may specifically request the Consultant to make additional site visits (Duty 66). Thus the role of the Consulting Engineer is largely that of technical adviser on design aspects.

44. The extent of supervisory responsibility described in LI79 is in general terms. The Landscape Consultant undertakes "to supervise the work by periodic inspection as he considers necessary to determine whether its progress and quality is generally in accordance with the contract. During his inspections he shall endeavour to guard his client against defects and deficiencies in the Contractor's work, but shall not be required to make exhaustive or continuous inspections of the work" (Clause 1.5).

45. Clause 1.6 of LI79 states that the Landscape Consultant "shall in no case be liable for work by the Contractor which may be either improperly executed or in breach of the terms of the contract; such liability in every case shall remain with the Contractor". This attempted disclaimer of liability for defective work is in similar terms to that of the architect under RIBA 82.

LEGAL LIABILITY OF THE SUPERVISOR

Contract

46. The legal liability of the Supervisor is determined by the terms of his contract of engagement with his client. When an action is brought against a Supervisor for failure to supervise in accordance with those terms, it will normally be necessary for the plaintiff to call independent expert evidence of the standards to be expected of a Supervisor in the particular circumstances (Sachs L.J. in Worboys v Acme Investments 4BLR133). How the courts have interpreted the duties of the Supervisor, can be determined by scrutiny of the judgments of the cases.

47. Where there is defective construction work, an employer will undoubtedly have a cause of action in damages against the Contractor. But the employer may also have a cause of action against the Supervisor for failing to detect the defective work. Judge Fay QC in Hutchinson v Harris (1978) described it thus: "It is a case of concurrent breaches of contract producing

the same damage. In my judgment the plaintiff has an action against both (builder and supervisor), although she cannot obtain damages twice over".

48. The courts may have the task of apportioning liability between the various defendants, under the Civil Liability (Contribution) Act 1978. Judge Fay QC gave some guidance on the apportionment in Eames London Estates v North Hertfordshire DC (1980) 18 BLR 50 when he indicated that "the blameworthiness of the policeman who fails to detect the crime is less than that of the criminal himself". But this is little comfort to the Supervisor who finds himself the sole defendant, the contractor having gone into liquidation (ref. 5).

Tort

49. The Supervisor may have a considerable liability in tort. The judgments in the leading case of Donoghue v Stevenson (1932) AC 562 include a statement by Lord Macmillam that "the categories of negligence are never closed". That statement has certainly proved true in relation to the liability of the Supervisor. One of the most recent illustrations is that of Junior Books v The Veitchi Co (1982) 21 BLR 66 in which a majority of the House of Lords appeared to "extend the duty of care beyond a duty to prevent harm being done by faulty work, to a duty to avoid such faults being present in the work itself".

50. One of the effects of an action in tort is that the six year limitation period runs from the date that the damage comes into existence (Pirelli v Oscar Faber 1982 21 BLR 99) rather than the date of the breach as in contract. Thus an action in tort may succeed in circumstances where an action in contract may be time-barred.

Statute

51. Liability of the Supervisor may also arise in statute. Some far-reaching obligations arise from the Health and Safety at Work Act 1974. One illustration of these obligations is provided by a case in which both a scaffolding sub-Contractor and a Local Authority were convicted, after a Health and Safety Executive inspector had noticed that scaffolding for a school building had been erected too close to an overhead power line. The Council's Supervisor knew of the danger and had decided to leave the situation over a weekend after failure to contact the Sub-Contractor. (ref. 6) More recently, in an accident which occurred at Carsington Reservoir, four people died when entering a manhole. Arising from that incident, the three partners of the firm of Consulting Engineers involved were fined as well as the Contractor. (ref. 7)

Extent of Supervisors Liability

52. The responsibility which a Resident Engineer may be involved in, is illustrated by the case of Thompson v Ellis, unreported, but referred to in the Presidential address of the late Sir Charles Husband to the Institution of Structural Engineers (ref. 8). In that case a Resident Engineer, late one night instructed steelwork Sub-Contractor's workmen not to lift a gearbox until the connection of a steel framework to which the lifting gear was fixed, had been bolted up. He then went home.

The workmen, ignoring the advice, proceeded with the lifting operation. Failure occurred, resulting in injury to one of the workmen who brought an action against the Sub-Contractor and the Consultant. Liability of the Consultant was held to be 60% and that of the steelwork Sub-Contractor 40%. In giving his decision the judge emphasised the responsibility of the Resident Engineer as the only professional man on the site at the time. He considered that it was not sufficient to have given the instruction, but that he should have stayed to see that his instruction was carried out.

53. The decision in the above case has generally been regarded as extreme. Probably a more accurate position of the law is represented by Clayton v Woodman 1962 4 BLR 65 in which the court held that the contractor and not the architect was fully responsible for how the work was carried out. A similar point arose in Oldschool v Gleeson 4 BLR 103 involving the collapse of a party wall during redevelopment work. Here, the Consulting Engineers were held not to have any duty to instruct the Contractor as to the manner of execution of the contract work.

54. Several cases have come before the courts in which the precise extent of an architects liability for detailed supervision of construction has been in dispute. In Leicester Board of Guardians v Trollope 1911 dry rot resulted from bad workmanship in that the timber joists were incorrectly supported. The architects argued that their duty was to supervise the general scheme, and that the detailed construction was the province of the Clerk of Works. The court held however that the defect was not a matter of detail. Channel J said "It does not seem to me that it excuses the architect from seeing that his design is complied with, that he thought that the Clerk of the Works would be sure to see that it was all right".

55. But defects may be matters of detail. In East Ham Corporation v Bernard Sunley (1966) AC 406 after completion of a school building, stone facings fell off and revealed defects in the fixings to the main structure. Lord Upjohn said "As is well known, the architect is not permanently on the site but appears at intervals, it may be of a week or a fortnight, and he has, of course, to inspect the progress of the work ... He may in such circumstances think that he knows the builder sufficiently well and can rely upon this to carry out a good job; that it is more important that he should deal with urgent matters on the site than that he should make a minute inspection of the site to see that the building is complying with the specification ... It by no means follows that, in failing to discover a defect which a reasonable examination would have disclosed, in fact the architect was necessarily thereby in breach of his duty to the building owner so as to be liable in an action for negligence."

56. The supervisory duty of the architect was again described by Judge Stabb QC in Sutcliffe v Chippendale and Edmondson 1971 18 BLR 149 thus "The building owner is entitled to expect his architect so to administer the contract and supervise the work,

as to ensure, as far as is reasonably possible, that the quality of work matches up to the standard contemplated". He also related the extent of supervision to the competence of the Contractor thus: "I think that the degree of supervision required of an architect must be governed to some extent by his confidence in the contractor. If and when something occurs which should indicate to him a lack of competence in the contractor, then in the interest of his employer, the standard of his supervision should be higher". This alone indicates that the cost of supervision cannot be determined in advance.

57. The recent case of <u>Kensington Chelsea and Westminster Area Health Authority v Adams Holden (1984 unpublished)</u> is an illustration of the apportionment of liability between the architect, clerk of works and structural engineer. Here, the fixing of precast mullions to the main structure of a hospital building failed some twelve years after construction. The plaintiff's action was against the architect and structural engineer in tort, since any claim in contract was time-barred. The structural engineer had not been engaged to supervise the erection of the mullions, but had checked the design of the fixings.

58. Judge Smout QC held that the structural engineer was not liable, and apportioned liability as architect 80% clerk of works 20%. The clerk of works had been employed by the plaintiff, but in accordance with the conditions of engagememt was "under the architect's direction and control". The judge found no evidence to displace the inference that the clerk of works was acting otherwise than as the servant of the building owner. Thus he found the plaintiff vicariously liable for the negligence of the clerk of works.

59. In the standard forms of construction contracts, the Supervisor has the duty to certify periodically the amounts of money properly due to the contractor. It is therefore important that his supervision is sufficient to enable him so to certify. Over-certification, which may occur if defective work remains undetected, can produce claims from the client particularly in the event of the contractor becoming insolvent as in <u>Sutcliffe v Thackrah (1974) 4 BLR 16</u>).

THE FUTURE

60. Any review of the standard Conditions of Engagement and the legal liabilities of the professional supervising construction work, invites the question "What of the future?"

61. Present indications both in the USA and UK are that the current level of legal actions will continue or increase (ref. 9). Raymond Cecil reported (ref. 10) that the number of claims submitted to insurers by architects in the UK, more than doubled between 1978 and 1982. Duncan Wallace has aptly commented that "we live in plaintiff's times, with the courts more than ready to find remedies wherever there is shown to be loss" (ref. 11).

62. Parallel with the increase in litigation is the move towards fee competition amongst professionals. Such competition, with demands to reduce costs of site supervision, must in due

course adversely affect quality of performance. This in turn must increase the risk of error and of defective work escaping unnoticed. Howell has asserted (ref. 3) that "we can directly correlate the frequency of professional liability (insurance) claims with the amount of construction review (supervision) being performed. The greater attentiveness to this important aspect of engineering, the lower the claim frequency". Thus using the terminology of Judge Fay's analogy, the blameworthiness of the policeman seems bound to increase as he fails to detect an increasing number of crimes, with his limited resources.

63. Duncan Wallace (ref. 11) believes that the standard forms of contract should be revised to limit the supervising services of the professionals to monitoring, in the owners interest only, compliance of the permanent works with the contract requirements ie. methods of working, temporary works etc. should be matters entirely for the contractor. He also advocates a radical re-examination of the contracts of engagement of the various parties to a construction project to define with greater precision their respective roles. He concludes that "professional contracts of employment will need to be re-examined and re-drafted".

64. However if it is to be regarded as reasonable that a client who suffers loss due to defective workmanship should be able to recover his loss from someone, yet unreasonable that the Supervisor should be liable for the whole of that loss in the event of a contractor going into liquidation, what is the solution? Many believe that limitation of liability is not acceptable nor that it is in the industry's long term interests. A system of project insurance has been advocated and would seem to have many attractions (ref. 12). Such an insurance would provide cover to all parties against all risks which may arise from design and construction, and would avoid disputes over apportionment of liability.

65. The British Property Federation (BPF) has recently published details of a completed revised system for building projects (ref. 13). It is significant that the system introduces a party called the Supervisor. Only time will tell whether such a system will succeed in changing the direction of the building industry. At the time of writing the standard agreement for the appointment of consultants for use under the BPF system, had not been published.

REFERENCES
1. Guidance Note 2A; Functions of the Engineer under the ICE Conditions of Contract. Ref. CCSJC/GN2AB/September 1977 issued by the ICE Conditions of Contract Standing Joint Committee.
2. Gilbert and Partners v Knight 4 BLR 9.
3. E.B. HOWELL: "Visions from a Crystal Ball" a paper presented to a conference held in San Diego in February 1981 on "Reducing

Risk and Liability through Better Specifications and Inspection" sponsored by the American Society of Engineers.

4. "Inspection of building structures during construction" Report by the Institution of Structural Engineers April 1983.

5. D.L. CORNES Design Liability in the Construction Industry. Granada 1983. 69.

6. "Health and Safety: The Resident Engineers Dilemma" The Journal of the Institution of Highway Engineers March 1980. p.23.

7. "Carsington Firms fined over gas deaths" New Civil Engineer 8/15 December 1983.

8. "The Increasing Responsibilities of the Structural Engineer" The Structural Engineer Vo. 42 No. 12 December 1964 p. 408-9.

9. J. SPRIGG DUVALL, Professional Indemnity. Consulting Engineer August 1980 p. 9-10.

10. R. CECIL, Liability. RIBA Journal July 1983 p.61.

11. I.N. DUNCAN WALLACE: Recent Canadian Cases - A Survey. 21 BLR.1.

12. OWEN LUDER: Solutions for Law of Liability. Building 20 January 1984, p.21.

13. "The BPF system for building design and construction" published by the British Property Federation 1983.

4 Management, contracting and package deals

G. D. G. COTTAM, BSc (Eng), FICE, Director, Marples International Ltd, Bath

MANAGEMENT CONTRACTING AND PACKAGE DEALS

Package Deals and Management Contracts are just two of the types of contract available for construction works - neither are a panacea for all works, but each has its role to play; nor are usual for civil engineering works. What they both have in common is the pre-eminent role of the Contractor and the need for the client to understand fully his role, because of the reduced role of the consultant, if they are to be successful.

Management Contracting

There is really nothing new about management contracting; it is really a logical extention of the cost-plus contract which has operated since Roman times, and probably even earlier.

Under the traditional system the client when he wishes to proceed with a construction or enterprise, appoints a professional advisor, an engineer or architect, who there-after designs the works, calls for tenders, advises on the appointment of the contractor, and usually supervises the works. The client may delegate to him most if not all the decision making, requiring only to be kept informed of the progress of the works and advised of any changes there may be in the costs. The client may also appoint directly a quantity surveyor to advise on the financial aspects of the project independently of the engineer or architect. Under a management contract the management contractor may take responsibility for all these roles, but will not necessarily undertake construction of the works himself. A total reverse of the normal roles!

There are a number of different systems for management contracting, all of which entail different contractual relationships between the parties. There are at present no standard published conditions of contract for management contracting, the nearest is probably the JET Prime Cost Contract.

The range of services that can be incorporated in management contracts are:

(a) Design:

(i)   Full responsibility
(ii) Management of a designer directly employed by the contractor
(iii) Co-ordination of the design, with designers employed by the client
(iv) Modify the design to accord with construction methods

(b) Pre-works Planning:

(i)   Budget costing, and construction cash flow
(ii) Funding arrangements
(iii) Preparation, issue of tender documents
(iv) Selection and appointment of contractors

(c) Construction:

(i)   Insurances
(ii)   Construction planning and programming
(iii) Design of temporary works and construction methods
(iv)   Procurement of materials
(v)   Provision of plant, offices and other services
(vi)   Supervision of the works
(vii) Quality control
(viii) Certification and payment of other contractors
(ix)   Cost control
(x)   Public relations and security

(d) Post Construction:

(i)   Assessment and settlement of claims
(ii) Maintenance supervision.

Under any form of management contract the role of the client is crucial. The major decisions will be made by the client, and he must expect the management contractor to be demanding in this regard. The client must set up a structure within his own organisation that defines clear limites of authority to each member of his staff to enable decisions to be arrived at speedily. The costs of delays are just as expensive under a management contract as they are under the traditional process.

The advantages claimed for management contracts over the traditional process are:

(a) The management contractor can be chosen at the outset of the design, and therefore input economical construction methods into the design
(b) There can be savings of time by starting construction before the design is complete; this time saving can

effect enourmous cost savings

(c) A better control can be exercised over the construction contractors

(d) Cost savings can be made by
  (1) Improvements in design detailing
  (2) Improved co-ordination of the design through a better understanding of the contractors "lead-in" times
  (3) Defining the construction contractors packages around their particular skills
  (4) Greater flexibility for design changes
  (5) Pre-planning the forward purchases of major essential materials
  (6) An improvement in the planning and co-ordination of the works
  (7) Improved cost control and financial forecasting
  (8) The establishment of industrial relations policies early in the contract.

The three main types of management contract are:

(a) Management contract
(b) Construction Management contract
(c) Design and Construction Management contract.

Management Contract

Under a simple management contract the contractor is responsible for the supervision of the works. The design is undertaken by a consultant in the traditional fashion, but the actual execution is carried out by other contractors (identified as Construction Contractors) under separate construction contracts placed with the approval of the client and directly with the client.

The co-ordination design with the construction is carried out by the client. It follows that the client must have staff trained in construction management for this relationship to work, and to a great extend this nulifies the benefits claimed for management contracting.

The management contractor is only performing the function usually performed by the Engineer. Its only advantage is that it separates supervision from design. The type of contract appears to provide little real advantage over the traditional methods, and would have little appeal for civil engineering works.

Construction Management Contracts (or Construction Manager)

The client at an early stage appoints a Construction Manager who will be responsible for the organisation and co-ordination of the design and the construction.

All the parties, the designers, the Construction Contractors and the Construction Manager will be under direct contract with the client. The Construction Manager can either be a firm or an individual.

This form of contract appears to offer little advantage over the traditional method, except for highly complicated works, with multiple principal designers.

Design and Management Contracts

The management contractor is responsible for both the design and the construction. The design may be undertaken either by in house design teams or by consultants under contract with the Management Contractor.

The client develops the initial scheme either himself in house, or by employing a consultant for the purpose. At the concept stage documents are worked up to sufficient detail to allow a Management Contractor to be appointed. This can either be by tender if there is sufficient detail, or by negotiation.

Once appointed the management contractor will work up the design and then construct the works under a series of construction contracts.

The advantages of this system can be that a better control is kept over the design with provision being made throughout for the contractors constructions methods. The priorities required by construction are more easily incorporated into the design process to enable smoother and speedier construction.

For the management contracting to be successful and the roles of the various parties and professions operating under the contract, must be understood by all parties if misunderstandings are not to nullify the advantages of the system.
(a) The client: to take full advantage of the flexibility of the system that is known to all parties and delegate responsibility to enable these decisions to be made, these contracts are complex and speedy. The Management Contractor must persuade, if necessary, the client to do so. It must be realised by the client that Management Contracts place a very heavy burden upon him, if the contract is to be successful.

(b) <u>The Management Contractor</u>: relationships between
Management Contractor and other parties will benefit if he is
appointed as early as possible, to avoid alternative relation
ships being established between the other parties. The
Management Contractor as a minimum is responsible for site
supervision and quality control. It is pointless for the
consultants to duplicate this activity. The Management
Contractor must be seen and be accepted as being in the
driving seat.
(c) <u>The Consultants</u>: their role is reduced to responsibility for the design and specification. Designers must
realise that they are part of a team and accept suggestions
and even instructions from the Management Contractor.

Conclusions

Management Contracting is widely used in the process
industry, sometimes in the building industry for the more
complex structures, but hardly at all in civil engineering.

It is at its most useful when speed is of the essence, and
where the design is not developed when construction starts,
neither of these factors generally apply to civil engineering
works, which usually have been in the pipeline for many years
before construction starts.

In order that the Management Contractor may have an interest
in the financial result of the project, consideration should
be given at the inception to the use of a Target Contract.
Under a Target Contract the contractor agrees an estimated
cost for the works with the client and shares any difference
between the actual costs of construction, and the estimated
costs with the client in agreed proportions. Mutual interest
in the financial results to the project engenders a sense of
common purpose which does much to remove any inherent mis-
trust between contractor and client.

It may however, be that engineers have maintained their role
as leaders of construction projects in civil engineering
projects because they have not abandoned the responsibility
for cost control in the manner of the architects. If
engineers do not in the future concentrate upon the management and financial aspects of construction as well as the
technical problems, then the role of "Engineer" under
construction contracts will increasingly be questioned,
generally to the benefit of Management Contractors.

PACKAGE DEALS

In a package deal, the contractor sells a produce not a
service; he therefore takes a certain responsibility for the
operation as well as the durability of the works.

The package deal is an extension of the design and construct management contract, but where the contractor may be responsible not only for the scope design of the work, but also the provision of finance for the project.

Included in the package can be any or all of the following:
(a)   Scope design
(b)   Detailed design
(c)   Construction
(d)   Commissioning
(e)   Management of the operation of the completed works or just recruitment of suitable staff
(f)   Finance for the project
(g)   Durability and performance guarantees.

The benefits of the package approach are that economy is produced both in design and construction from the previous experiences of the contractor. The project may be completed in the minimum time due to the unification of design, specification and construction. The risk to the client is reduced because the contractor takes responsibility for the entire project.

The package approach is widely used for housing, warehouse and farming design, process engineering, manufacturing plants power stations and specialist facilities.

The main advantages of the package approach are minimum time of construction at minimum cost. The client puts much faith in the contractor and it is essential that he agrees before the contract award, the specification, particularly the finishes of the works. It is natural that the client should require some form of assurances that what he is purchasing is both suitable and acceptable. He should resist the temptation to appoint a plethora of advisors to check the design, specification and construction, but rely upon enforceable guarantees both to quality and performance. The surest way to disaster will be to appoint leading consultants to act as checking authorities as they will try to enforce their own specifications with the result that delays and claims for additional costs will be inevitable. A package is a package and it is important that the implications of this are fully realised by the client.

There are no standard conditions for package deals, although both the National Federation of Building Trades Employers, and the Joint Contractors Tribunal produce Design and Construction Standard Forms.

Most package deals are executed upon the amendments to the normal standard conditions of contract, or upon conditions specially written for the contract. Since conditions of each

package vary considerably it is inevitable that any standard
form would require a large number of special conditions
which would make the ideal of a Standard Contract impractical.

The movement towards both the package deal and management
contract will continue particularly in the Developing World,
after all, what other industry separates responsibility for
design and construction with the same definity as the
construction industry. The division benefits the professions
but not the client. In developing countries pressure from
Third World Contractors will force the contractors from the
Developed Nations to adopt this approach if they are to
compete successfully. At home, Management Contracts must
develop such that the Management Contractors accept full
responsibility for both the durability and operation of the
works over an extended period. However, a contract is only
as successful as the parties make it, and for the client
both Management Contracts and Package Deal contracts involve
placing a high degree of faith in the appointed Contractor.
It follows that much time and effort should be expended upon
the selection of the Contractor.

If the client has sufficient in-house expertise he should
undertake the selection himself, otherwise he should appoint
an advisor for this specific function. The expert can be an
Engineer, and Architect or a Quantity Surveyor. The choice
should depend upon the parameters of greatest importance for
the success of a project, and technical expertise will
usually take precedence over financial considerations at
this stage.

The appointment of the advisor should terminate upon the
selection of the contractor to avoid a possible clash which
would prejudice the relationship during the construction.

The selection process should go through the following stages:

(a) List of possible contractors - list of suitable
     contractors experienced in the type of work, should
     have 20-30 names. They may be selected from a number
     of sources - Trade Lists, personal experience or those
     who have written expressing an interest;

     The list should then be examined and reduced to 10-12
     and the firms contacted for confirmation of interest.
     These firms can then be interviewed with a view to both
     informing the contractors of the project and seeking
     advice from them concerning their opinion on the best
     arrangements for the project.

(b) The Short List - following the meetings the list should
     be reduced to 3-4 and a brief definition of the clients
     requirements drawn up.

(c)   The Enquiry - this brief should cover interalia:
description of the project; the clients performance
requirements; date of completion etc; the proposed
contractual relationships between all parties; the
extent of the contractors responsibility; the principles
of the tender sought.

(d)   Evaluation - after submission of formal offers, the
tenderers should be interviewed and asked for further
information particularly concerning their proposed staff
for the works. Construction is always only as good as
the people undertaking it.

Once the client has satisfied himself on the technical
competence and financial structure of the tendering
companies, he can then select his contractor on price. For
technical competence is more important than a marginal price
saving on the management fee.

Clients must realise the input required from them under the
Management Contracts, and Package Deals. Fortunately, the
situations in which these contractual arrangements are most
successful are when the works themselves are complex or
technically involved, and in both cases the client should
have this expertise.

5 Supervision of the contract programme

M. BARNES, BSc (Eng), PhD, FICE, FCIOB, MBCS, ACIArb, Senior Partner, Martin Barnes and Partners, Stockport, Cheshire

SYNOPSIS. The construction contractor is allowed control over his own construction programme, provided he finishes on time. However, adherence to the programme should be monitored and supervised in the same way as adherence to the drawings and specification is monitored and supervised on behalf of the Employer. The paper analyses how the contractor's programme can be monitored using the ICE Conditions of Contract. Recommendations for improved methods are set out and likely future developments discussed.

INTRODUCTION

1. Management of construction work involves control and supervision of the three interlinked components - performance, cost and time. A completed building or work of civil engineering can be judged by its:-

Performance - Was the design right?
                  Was it built in accordance with the design?

Cost   - Was the budget right?
                  Was it built within the budget?

Time   - Was the programmed completion date right?
                  Was it completed on time?

2. If the answer to all six questions is yes, the project was very effectively managed and supervised. It is the answer to the second question in each pair which exposes the effectiveness of supervision. It is part of the duty of the professionals acting for the Employer that they should take all reasonable steps to ensure that construction work is carried out in accordance with the design and that it is completed within budget and on time. This is a paraphrase of the duties written out variously in the conditions of engagement of architects, engineers and quantity surveyors and in the job descriptions of clerks of works and resident engineers. Is is a principle fundamental to their appointments which establishes the nature of the supervision on behalf of the Employer which is the subject of this paper.

3. Supervision of adherence to the programme has a special characteristic which makes it more difficult than the other two. If work is done which is not in accordance with the

design, it can be removed and replaced. If more money than
planned is spent upon some work, the Contractor can be required to pay for it himself, leaving the cost to the Employer
unaffected. Buf if the Contractor finishes later than planned,
the delay inevitably impacts upon the Employer. The clock can
not be put back whilst the Contractor tries again to hit the
date, neither can the Contractor himself absorb a time over-run
as he can a cost over-run. For this reason, it is important to
supervise the timing of construction as far as possible on the
basis of prevention of delays rather than cure. There is no
opportunity for a second try or for passing the problem created
by a delayed completion to another party. Liquidated damages
for delay do not provide an effective remedy.

4. The programme is the time plan in the same sense as the
drawings and specification are the performance plan. Programme
supervision is directed to adherence to the programme in the
same sense as performance supervision is directed to adherence
to the drawings and specification. Programme supervision comprises monitoring the production and use of programmes by the
Contractor (and sub-contractors). It is of comparable importance to supervision of performance when the Employer's objectives in commissioning a construction project include achievement
of completion in a short time, to a crucial deadline, or both.
Few modern projects can afford the luxury of the pursuit of
highest possible technical quality or even of greatest economy
if these are to be achieved at the expense of delay or uncertainty of completion date.

5. The subject is discussed in this paper mainly in the context of a civil engineering project carried out using the ICE
Conditions of Contract, fifth edition, June 1973, revised January 1979.

THE CONTRACTOR'S TIME COMMITMENT

6. Under most standard conditions of contract the Contractor
undertakes to complete the Works within a period of time stated
in the Contract. This period starts when the instruction to
begin work is given. Except where sections of the work have a
later start date or a shorter completion period, the arrangement of the programme within the stated period is totally at
the Contractor's discretion. The requirement in the ICE Conditions Clause 41 that the Contractor should "proceed with the
Works with due expedition and without delay" does not hamper
this discretion as the only real test of whether the requirement
is being met is whether the Contractor is working to his own
programme. It would not be a breach of Clause 41, for example,
if a Contractor planned not to start work on site for some
while due to a long lead time on delivery of a particular material or item of specialised plant.

7. It is only the existence of a programme furnished by the
Contractor which enables the likelihood of completion on time
to be monitored on behalf of the Employer by his supervisors.
Without it, the Employer could only stand back and hope. He
would have to accept whatever reassurances the Contractor

offered if it began to seem more and more likely that the work
was not going to be finished on time. It follows that the
provisions for monitoring the Contractor's performance against
his own programme established in the Contract are the basis
for supervision of timing on behalf of the Employer. The standard conditions of contract used in the building industry had
no such provisions before 1980. In the new JCT Conditions of
Contract the Contractor is now required to submit a programme
but there are no provisions for using it in any way after it
has been submitted. The requirement for a programme to exist
at all is a step in the right direction, but leaves building
practice some way behind civil engineering practice. Clause
14 of the ICE Contract provides for the submission and use of
a programme to help supervise the timing of construction within the completion period. Its strengths and weaknesses are
discussed in the next section.

THE CLAUSE 14 PROGRAMME

8. Within three weeks of acceptance of his tender, the Contractor is required to submit a programme to the Engineer
which shows the "order of procedure in which he proposes to
carry out the Works". This phrase detracts from the common-
sense meaning of the word "programme". However, if the submitted programme omits any information which the Engineer has
reason to require, he may ask for it to be furnished. At the
same time the Contractor has to provide a "general description of the arrangements and methods of construction" which he
proposes to adopt. The programme is submitted to the Engineer
"for his approval" but nothing is said about what happens if
the Engineer does not approve it, either through finding
something in it of which he disapproves or simply through
ignoring it. There is no sanction upon the Contractor which
induces him to submit a programme in the first place and no
inducement to seek it's approval. It is not surprising that
in many civil engineering contracts the "Clause 14 Programme"
is submitted late and that it is often not approved before
variations and other unexpected circumstances have made its
approval irrelevant.

9. Where a contractor has submitted a programme with his
tender, the incentive to get a detailed and realistic programme approved under the provisions of Clause 14 is further
reduced. For example, the tender programme can be used to
establish the dates by which outstanding information must be
provided if delay is to be avoided. Approval means little
even when it is obtained as it creates no stated obligation
on the Contractor to work to the programme and, by virtue of
Clause 14(7) does not affect any other obligations he may
have. Despite these shortcomings, Clause 14 produces the
effect that a programme usually does exist against which the
Contractor's progress can be compared and the likelihood of
delayed completion forecast.

10. If progress falls behind, the Engineer may ask for a
revised programme to be produced but, strangely, the Contract

does not require this to be submitted for approval. The clause which provides for revision of the programme in theory cannot operate unless the original programme has been approved and it does not provide properly for revision of a programme which has already been revised. The effect of these shortcomings is to make the status of the current programme vague and to leave the Engineer with no power to use it to influence the Contractor towards achieving the completion date during construction.

CLAUSES 13, 46 AND 51

11. Other routes for influencing the timing of construction are provided by Clauses 13, 46 and 51 but, unfortunately, they also end in something of a fog. Clause 13(1) empowers the Engineer to issue instructions and directions on matters which may include methods and speed of construction. The Contractor is obliged to "adhere strictly" to any such instructions and directions and has an over-riding obligation to carry on the Works such that the "mode manner and speed" of construction are to be "of a kind and in a manner approved of by the Engineer". The provision in Clause 13(3) entitles the Contractor to be paid extra if complying with an instruction given under Clause 13(1) causes delay or cost "beyond that reasonably to have been foreseen by an experienced contractor at the time of tender". It is here that the fog begins to descend. Who can say whether an experienced contractor would have foreseen that, in the event of falling behind programme, the Engineer would have given a particular instruction for speeding up which would have led to particular additional costs such as overtime or additional plant? Such things are most unlikely to have been specifically foreseen but could have been contemplated in general terms. The result of this vagueness is that Engineers seldom issue instructions under Clause 13 which are intended to enforce recovery of lost time.

12. Under Clause 46 the Engineer may notify the Contractor if he thinks that work is going too slowly to finish on time. On receiving such a notice the Contractor must take such steps as are necessary to speed up and ensure prompt completion. The Engineer is supposed to approve the steps taken. This notification is little more than a reminder of the Contractor's existing obligations. It is questionable whether approval by the Engineer of the Contractor's proposed steps to speed up implies that the Engineer considers them sufficient to ensure prompt completion. If this implication is intended, approval by the Engineer could be taken as easing the Contractor's obligation to complete on time, if it turns out that the approved steps were not enough. This implication is supported by the fact that there is no eliminating disclaimer like the one expressly stated in Clause 14(7) with respect to the approval of the originally planned methods and programme. However, as the Conditions do not say what happens if the Engineer does not approve the proposed steps, not to approve them is probably the prudent course.

13. Clause 51 empowers the Engineer to order variations to the "specified sequence method or timing of construction (if any)". This power might also be used to press a tardy Contractor to greater speed by ordering faster methods or simply faster timing of construction than that specified. Unfortunately, the clause implies that it is not within the Engineer's power to specify methods or timing of construction where no methods or timing were specified before. This route to influence over the Contractor's timing of the work turns out also to be barred in normal circumstances.

14. In summary, the supervision of the contract programme is not fully provided for by the ICE Conditions. The Employer must rely mainly upon the Contractor's own internal incentives to finish on time and upon the incentive created by the liquidated damages provisions. The contractor's principal internal incentive is that of carrying out work at a fast pace in order to minimise time-related indirect costs. This is often more than sufficient incentive upon the Contractor and the large proportion of civil engineering contracts which are finished on time reflects the managerial effort which is often brought to bear upon the achievement of programmed times by contractors.

SUPPLEMENTING THE CONTRACTUAL PROVISION FOR PROGRAMME MONITORING

15. Increasingly Employers are supplementing their rights to supervise the programme either by adding special conditions of contract or by specifying additional programming requirements. An example of the former is given in the Appendix to this paper. This comprises the text of instructions to tenderers for supplying a programme with the tender and requirements for the information it should contain. Also shown are two special conditions of contract. The first requires the appointed Contractor to provide a programme in similar form to the tender programme to act as his Clause 14 programme. The second requires the Contractor to provide a weekly progress report related to this programme. The two special conditions are worded to avoid the problems of approval of programmes, lack of relationship of Clause 14 to a tender programme and obscurity of the outcome of application of Clause 13(1) which were discussed in the previous section.

16. The Special Conditions also require the timing of any work covered in the Bill of Quantities by method-related charges to be identified on the Clause 14 programme. This arrangement effects the link between programme, contract prices and proposed methods of construction which is helpful to Engineer and Contractor when assessing interim payments and when valuing those variations which affect timing and construction method. The Special Conditions are worded to leave the Contractor maximum flexibility in his choice of programming medium. It is important that a plan should be made as a result of a careful synthesis but it matters little whether it is expressed as a bar chart or a network and still

less whether the network is an arrow diagram or a precedence diagram. It is becoming commonplace for Employers or their Engineers to specify the programming medium which the Contractor is to use in very fine detail which is to be deprecated. It can lead to contractors having to subcontract their programming and reporting work to specialists who operate the particular computer system which can produce exactly the reports specified. It is much better for the Employer that Contractors should be able to use the programming medium with which they are familiar so that the real work of planning can be undertaken thoroughly. Detailed specifications of programming medium also tend to stifle development of improved systems by standardising upon the more widely-used. Precedence diagram networks are much easier to learn and use than arrow diagrams, but many specifications can only be met by the older arrow diagram form.

17. The Special Conditions set out in the Appendix allow the Contractor very wide flexibility of choice of programming medium - from a hand drawn bar chart with principal sequence links added to a computer plotted network of either of the two principal forms. The progress report information is defined sufficiently basically that it can be produced by almost any manual or computerised programming system being operated by the Contractor and can be used as input to almost any system which is being used by or on behalf of the Employer. The progress report concentrates upon information about remaining work. This is a deliberate emphasis designed to help concentrate management attention on that which can yet be controlled - the future. It may be only a short step for programme and progress information to be exchanged automatically between the computers used by the Contractor and the Employer. At the moment this could only be achieved if both parties were using the same planning software on the same computer hardware, still an unlikely coincidence. With the impending development of machine independent data transmission (such as the DIAL System being developed by BSI) the convenience of automatic exchange may be available quite soon.

MONITORING RESOURCES AND COSTS

18. A logical extension of supervision of the contract programme, concerned as it is only with time, is to supervise by monitoring a set of information which is a "model" of resources, methods, cost and time. Such a model is a combination of a programme and an estimate which can be used to assess the effect upon cost and time of variations, of any other changes to the work itself and changes to the circumstances in which it is done. Such a model could take the place of both the contract programme and the priced bill of quantities in both control and supervision of construction work. Suitable software has been available for some time but has not yet been used contractually in this way. A trial using a time/cost modelling system as the basis for supervision of the Contractor's programme and resource usage is

currently under way on a trunk road scheme near Carmarthen.
Here the system being used is the PCM (Project Cost Model)
computer system operated on an on-site mini computer. The
trial was commissioned by the Department of Transport and is
being carried out by Howard Humphreys & Partners with assistance from Project Software Limited who supplied the software.

SUPERVISION OR CONTROL?

19. In all aspects of project management, the people
involved must clearly distinguish between the responsibilities
of supervision and of control. A well ordered management
scheme will unequivocally place responsibility for control
with the party best able to exert it by means of foresighted
and well-informed decision making. It will also provide for
supervision or monitoring of the control function by another
party. Thus the Contractor should be left as far as possible
to make his own decisions about construction methods and timing so that he should be unequivocally in control of them.
Supervision of his plans should provide a backstop or "belt
and braces" without infringing upon his responsibility for
control. This is why contracts have to contain clauses which
provide that "approval does not diminish responsibility" not
only as regards programmes and method statements but as
regards technical supervision of the quality of the work. It
often seems unfair to contractors that they are supervised
but that the supervisor takes none of the blame when things
go wrong. Unfortunately it is a feature of the system which
is unavoidable if allocation of responsibility is not to
become hopelessly confused.

20. Resident engineers and inspectors will occasionally
condemn work which they watched being carried out a few days
before and Engineers will occasionally approve a Contractor's
programme which assumes a monumentally impractical construction method. It must be hoped that there will continue to be
very few of these events in comparison with the number of
occasions when perceptive supervision pre-empts wasteful
expense and delay. This is to the benefit of both the Contractor and the Employer.

APPENDIX

Instructions to tenders and special conditions of contract
intended to reinforce provision for supervision of the
contract programme

INSTRUCTION TO TENDERERS

It is of primary importance to the Employer that the
construction of the Works should be completed in accordance
with the times for completion entered in the Appendix to the
Form of Tender. To this end tenderers are required to plan
the work during the tender period and to submit details of

their plans with their tenders. The Employer may reject a tender which is not supported by a practical and detailed programme for assembling and operating the resources necessary to complete the Works on or before the required dates.

The attention of tenderers is drawn to Clauses 73 and 74 of the Conditions of Contract.

Each tender is to be accompanied by a programme showing:-

(a) each site operation requiring the use of a separate team of plant and/or labour as a separate activity;

(b) the assumed limitations upon the sequence of activities and the anticipated start and completion times for the activities in weeks numbered from the Date for Commencement of the Works;

(c) the number nature and size of the plant and/or labour teams which it is anticipated shall be used on each activity;

(d) the times at which any costs covered in the Bill of Quantities by Fixed Charges are expected to be incurred and the time periods over which any costs covered in the Bill of Quantities by Time-Related Charges are expected to be incurred and

(e) a description of the proposed methods of construction referring to the nature and extent of Temporary Works.

SPECIAL CONDITIONS OF CONTRACT

The following special conditions form part of the Conditions of Contract.

TENDER PROGRAMME

73. The Contractor shall not be bound to construct the Works in accordance with the programme submitted with his Tender but the Engineer may in carrying out his duties under Clauses 13, 14 and 46 require the Works to be constructed in accordance with a programme no less favourable to the interests of the Employer than that submitted by the Contractor with his Tender.

PROGRAMME

74(1) The programme submitted in accordance with Clause 14(1) and any revised programme produced in accordance with Clause 14(2) shall show:-

(a) each site operation requiring the use of a separate team of plant and/or labour as a separate activity;

(b) the assumed limitations upon the sequence of activities and the anticipated start and completion times for the activities in weeks numbered from the Date for Commencement of the Works;

(c) the number nature and size of the plant and/or labour teams which it is anticipated shall be used on each activity;

(d) the times at which any costs covered in the Bill of Quantities by Fixed Charges are expected to be incurred and the time periods over which any costs covered in the Bill of Quantities by Time-Related Charges are expected to be incurred; and

(e) a description of the proposed methods of construction referring to the nature and extent of Temporary Works.

74(2) At the end of each week following submission of the programme in accordance with Clause 14(1) until the final Certificate of Completion has been issued the Contractor shall submit to the Engineer's Representative in writing a progress report comprising:-

(a) a list of those activities shown on the current programme which were begun during the week stating their remaining durations in weeks and their anticipated completion times;

(b) a list of those activities begun previously upon which work continued during the week stating their remaining durations in weeks and their anticipated completion times;

(c) a list of those activities begun previously but upon which no work was carried out during the week stating their remaining durations in weeks and their anticipated completion times; and

(d) a list of the activities completed during the week.

If the anticipated completion time of any activity reported is later than that reported previously or where not reported previously later than the completion time shown on the current programme the circumstances which in the opinion of the Contractor have caused the anticipated delay shall be stated. Any other matters not previously reported which in the opinion of the Contractor may cause delay to the current programme shall be described. The current programme is the revised programme last produced in accordance with Clause 14(2) and submitted to the Engineer or where no revised programme has been submitted the original programme submitted in accordance with Clause 14(1).

6

Supervision and insurance

K.E.O. GRIFFITHS, Senior Partner, Griffiths & Armour, Liverpool

1.   How do Insurers view the contract clauses related to supervision and the effect of these on claims: are there lessons to be learned?

2   In two words: 'seriously' and 'yes'.

3   It is over thirty years since my children read Enid Blyton's adventure stories and I don't doubt that the Inventor who always featured in them would very often turn out to be a Consulting Engineer if she was alive and writing today.

4   She managed to portray him as a fascinatingly eccentric wild-haired and sometimes wild-tempered unworldly figure who dreamt up earth-shattering schemes from his remote fastness.

5   He did his own drawings and calculations no doubt, but one never read of his supervisory role or involvement in the letting of contracts.

6   A hundred years earlier when Stephenson, Brunel and Telford engineered our heritage of highways, canals and railways the roles of Principal, Consultant and Contractor were not demarcated as closely as they are today and the designer felt free to intervene in the execution of his design as he saw necessary.

7   Up to the end of the 1940s individual firms of Consulting Engineers had their own Conditions of Contract and until the mid 1960s the bulk of the profession was concentrated within the area between the Palace of Westminster and Victoria Station.

8   Things have changed beyond recognition during the working lifetime of most of today's senior Engineers whether they be Consultants, Contractors or Employer's Engineers and the meaning of the word 'supervision' must be seen from the standpoint of the Engineers as they understood it when it first found its way into the wording of the ICE Conditions. At that time firms were smaller, partner/staff ratios were higher, design and drawing offices were smaller, the Contractor assumed a different role in the design process, established trades operated within the limits of a smaller corpus of knowledge and an arguably greater corpus of skill, inflation and costs were within manageable limits and the claim-making profession had not developed.

9   The wheel of progress has turned through 180° since then and continues to turn; however, when it reaches the 360° mark the ground-plan will have changed in its turn.

Supervision of Construction. Thomas Telford Ltd, London, 1985

10   When the ICE Conditions first appeared the word 'super-vision' was used against a background of common understanding as to its meaning in the context of resources and expertise available; since then it has been interpreted through a process of decision and evolution to the stage where currently about one-sixth of professional negligence claims against Consulting Engineers are based upon allegations of faulty or inadequate supervision.

11   Thus the insurance market must view the issue of supervision seriously.

12   The Contractor's obligation is to 'construct complete and maintain' the works and to 'take full responsibility for the adequacy stability and safety of all site operations and methods of construction' (other than the design or specification of the Permanent Works and of any Temporary Works designed by the Engineer). The Contractor has to give or provide 'all necessary superintendence' by sufficient persons having adequate knowledge. It is his responsibility to ensure that workmanship and materials are of the respective kinds described in the Contract and in accordance with the Engineer's instructions.

13   To saddle the party who contracts to provide physical works with such obligations seems entirely reasonable and to accord with concepts of natural justice.

14   The Engineer offers his client services, not physical works.

15   The Engineer is bound to his client by Conditions of Engage-ment: he undertakes inter alia to 'satisfy himself that the Works are executed generally according to the contract and otherwise in accordance with good engineering practice', to witness specified tests, to approve the materials, plant and labour provided by the Contractor and the mode manner and speed of construction: where there is an Engineer's Representative his functions are to 'watch and supervise'.

16   My Concise Oxford Dictionary defines supervise thus .....
"oversee, superintend execution or performance of (thing) or actions or work of (person)". To oversee is defined as "superin-tend...", but superintend is decined as "have the management of, arrange and inspect working of" and thus before we venture into the English/French, English/Spanish or English/German diction-aries we have already found the Engineer's Representative's head in a potentially uncomfortable noose.

17   When the ICE Conditions were first drafted and the word 'supervision' was incorporated there was no such word as Qango but my Concise Oxford Dictionary contains it, nor did 'hassles' exist but we all know too well what they are now; hence we must attempt to look into the minds of the drafters working as they were within the knowledge and concepts of their time.

18   Given the resources available to the Consultant of that time I suspect that if those conditions were being written today the drafters might have opted for the words 'monitor' or 'inspect' in their contemporaneous usage.

19   In my own business of insurance much midnight oil has been burnt over recent years toward the goal of expressing policies in so-called Plain English and the protagonists have always been met

with opposition from those who have stated with some justification that the meaning of established policy wordings has been determined over the centuries by the interpretations of judges and only a foolish man tampers with them: but where meaning may have been stretched outwith the bounds of intent it might be deemed wise to convene and confer with the aim of better expressing that intent. In your profession I would commend the word 'supervision' as being worthy of such attention.

20 It must be remembered that many more claims arise and are settled by agreement between the parties than ever see the Court with its attendant costs and the notorious risk of submitting what seemed like a bullet-proof case to the rigours of judgment.

21 My firm conducted an exhaustive enquiry into a representative selection of claims made against professional Engineers as at January 1983 and out of that selection as many as one-third had to do with alleged failures of supervision.

22 Not all claims result in a payment to the claimant but all of them result in worry and non-productive work to the detriment of the practice's existing workload and the search for new work, and they must bring the matter of reputation and credibility into question. Does one attempt to curry favour and 'goodwill' by buying such claims out as they are made, or does one accept that sometimes the obligation to hold the line rests with oneself and steel oneself to fighting for the cause one knows to be right and to be in the longer term interest of the profession? One may well carry insurance and one is unwise if not irresponsible if one does not, but Underwriters are custodians of a common fund of premium, not of a bottomless crock of gold. Claims paid mean premiums to be paid.

23 Even a successful passage through the Courts does not mean that all one's costs and losses are awarded.

24 To be joined in an Action at all, even maybe as fourth or fifth Defendant, can in an extreme case result in one's financial responsibility bearing little proportion to one's contribution to the circumstances which led up to the Action. Where, for example a Contractor, a sub-contractor and an Architect are all ahead of the Engineer in the list of Defendants and the first two go into liquidation and the Architect proves to have little or no professional indemnity coverage and no substantial personal wealth it will fall upon the Engineer's insurers and perhaps ultimately on the Engineer and his partners personally to make good the balance of the judgment sum. The adoption of limited liability status by professional firms would protect against personal insolvency in such cases unless the Courts saw fit to see through such limitation - as has been seen in recent instances where DHSS have pursued claims for unpaid employees' NI contributions against directors personally - but within the UK context and perceptions of professional practice such a course would need to be viewed from a wider angle.

25 In addition to the 'joint tortfeasors' problem there are the particular and very real problems which have been posed by the age of recession and inflation which we hope may now be giving

way to a healthier economic climate. The Employer may have
embarked upon a project which with hindsight, high interest and
low potential return he wishes he had never begun and the
Contractor, desperate for turnover, may have put in a price
which as the contract progresses and costs escalate he lives to
regret, or indeed goes under. In circumstances such as these it
is little wonder that the industry of claim-making took root and
prospered and that both parties should be gunning for the
professionals.

26   Subject to interpretation as it evolves of what 'supervision'
entails the legal obligations arise in both contract and tort.
A claim brought in contract has an ascertainable time limitation
and the contract may also limit the quantum - vide the FIDIC
Conditions of Engagement where the Consultant's liability is
limited to the fees. However, if the claim can be framed in
negligence and action is brought in that tort then quantum
limitations do not exist and the time limitation is passing
through throes of considerable uncertainty. With the 1976 case
of Sparham Souter -vs- Town & Country Developments closely
followed in 1977 with Anns & others -vs- Merton London Borough
Council the Consulting Engineer was literally at risk for an
indefinite period plus another seven years for service of the
Writ, or thirteen years for an English contract under seal. The
position has improved since the judgment in the case of Pirelli
-vs- Oscar Faber in that occurrence of damage sets the time clock
running rather than the fact of discovering damage.

27   There is quite clearly a need to bring some greater certainty
into the matter of liability for negligence: if not as to quantum
at least as to the Limitation of actions. The topic has been the
subject of deliberation for several years but no conclusion has
yet been propounded which is acceptable to all the interests
involved. In UK the private consumer has been distinguished from
the commercial consumer inter alia in the matter of housebuilding
by the NHBC scheme and in the relief granted in matters of
innocent non-disclosure to Underwriters of marine, aviation and
transport insurance and the Unfair Contract Terms Act of 1977
enshrines the distinction. In the Napoleonic Code a period of
ten years' strict liability is imposed upon the construction team
for failure of major structural elements from the date of
practical completion and a two year period of strict liability
applies in the case of 'menus ouvrages' which includes such
matters as paintwork. The context of the legislation clearly
envisages essentially building work if not solely private housing
and its extension into the field of civil engineering poses
obvious problems where the operation of complex plant is in the
hands of the user and misuse or abuse is outwith the control of
Consultant and Contractor. So-called appropriate technology -
perhaps labour-intensive to provide employment at a level
unacceptable in a sophisticated economy, or simple by the
omission of state-of-the-art control systems beyond the servicing
capabilities of remote and impoverished Third World countries -
can easily be mistaken as a slight by potentates who demand the
latest and the best. My elder son has been to an equatorial
African capital which boasted a high-rise hotel but no power to

operate the lifts nor to raise the water which had to be carried by hand. Today's newest electronic gadgetry may well be manufactured by a 'boom and bust' operation which has been liquidated and forgotten before the expiration of a statutory limitation period, leaving the remaining parties to pick up the resultant claims in strict liability which may be hard to justify in equity.

28 Thus whilst a properly financed guarantee system such as NHBC may be appropriate for the protection of individuals as the bottom rung in a property-owning democracy its extension to cover Principals who may have the power to levy a rate or taxes across a broad base is hardly appropriate and arguably unnecessary.

29 Equally, a system of Decennial insurance in which the sums at risk mount on grounds more hypothetical than realistic until after ten years the total value at risk requires that it be underwritten by a pool of Insurers can only add costs which may be deemed inappropriate to the value thereby purchased. And by the creation of a pool the competition and innovation which a competitive market-place provides have been lost.

30 Simplistic ideas of consumer protection are thus a misleading signpost to the resolution of the problem. They may have their place in the 'consumer' market-place but their extension into realms where the consumer has resources infinitely greater than those of the providers would be unsoundly based.

31 Having tried to place the problem in its context let me now turn to some of the practicalities of supervision and then to the insurance of one's failures in this regard.

32 To start with the design stage:

a) What systems of check are operated within the Office? Is every drawing and calculation subjected to a second check by someone other than the draughtsman who is qualified to make that check more than a mere formality? Is it carried out by a Partner or by a qualified senior Engineer? How is it evidenced that such a check has been carried out? What mechanism exists to ensure that other persons of appropriate discipline within the Firm have the chance to express their view? What mechanism exists to ensure that all needful checks have been carried out and evidenced before a drawing leaves the office?

b) Who checks the computer solution against the slide-rule? How is it evidenced that such a check has indeed been made?

c) Have your younger Engineers had the opportunity to supplement their theoretical knowledge with practical experience? Are they so heavily metricated as not to understand conventional measure which will almost certainly be used on site? Do they appreciate the problems of carrying out precise work at great depth or height in extreme weather and have they ever tried to do so? If a workman on site drills an oval hole instead of a round one to achieve a precise union is their structure intrinsically strong enough to withstand a measure of 'bodging'? Will their design have sufficient strength to withstand likely pre-completion loads through the importation of plant and machinery during the process of construction?

73

d) Has the client's acceptance of decisions made at the design stage been secured and confirmed in writing? Expendion soil surveys can be a bone of great contention - if all proves sound the Engineer may be held to have wasted money, yet if the ground proves unsound the Engineer ought to have specified proper tests. Has the decision been fully and formally recorded? Has the air-conditioning and heating been designed on the basis that reflective curtains be fitted - and if so has the fact been duly recorded? Instances in this field are legion.

e) How is the practice proposing to face up to self-certification for purposes of Building Regulations? Like every privilege it imposes its obligations, and with the removal of an independent check it reinforces the need for extra vigilance in one's internal systems of check. The potential for undetected design error is enhanced. Will it impose a new obligation given by the Engineer to the Authority on whose behalf the certification is given and how will one assess the quantum of damages in the event of a claim from this source? Insofar as self-certification is concerned the answer would appear to be within the ambit of current Professional Indemnity insurance. However, in the terms of the Building Control Bill which is due for Royal Assent in the early summer of 1984 firms may be interested in becoming "Approved Certifiers", involving checking the designs of others and checking the construction. They will be required to hold professional indemnity insurance for £1m each & every claim, with an uninsured excess not exceeding £200, and it will have to be a 15 year cover. If the insurance requirements can be made acceptable to the Underwriting profession who will be asked to bear the risk then firms may opt to become 'Approved Certifiers' and will have to effect the appropriate cover. Precisely how and to what extent the certification of actual construction is to be carried out in practice is a matter worthy of the most careful consideration and definition. I shall in paragraph 40 turn some light onto the topic of warranties and guarantees which are potentially implicit in a certification process.

33 During the construction phase the question of supervision becomes even more highlighted and some points to be borne prominently in mind are:

a) Has formal agreement been negotiated with the client as to the number and frequency of site visits and has such agreement been recorded?

b) Are the Engineer and the Client agreed and recorded as such as to the procedure for examining work before covering up in the event that work is not on schedule and additional expenditure has to be incurred by the Engineer for such an inspection?

c) Have the Engineer and the Client agreed as to whether or not a Resident Engineer be appointed? If such an appointment is to be made have the parties recorded their accord as to his payment and as to responsibility for his actions, failures and decisions and as to his chain of reporting?

Would the documentation of such accord stand scrutiny in
the event of a problem arising at a future date?
d) What duty rests upon the Engineer in respect of work
which is not his direct responsibility? Is he to 'interfere'
and perhaps engage himself in a liability thereby, or turn a
blind eye and be held to have been negligent?
e) Has the firm grasped the full implications of the Health
& Safety at Work &c Act? How do they view their responsibility for site safety in the light of the Act irrespective of
the Contract Conditions' imposition of such responsibility
solely on the Contractor. Only recently we have seen the
individual Partners of a Consulting firm fined albeit the
circumstances may hardly have been such as to set too rigid
a precedent.
f) Can the sole practitioner reasonably undertake the full
consultancy role including supervision? It does of course
depend upon the man and upon the nature and number of
engagements he undertakes, but there are circumstances when
the sole practitioner would do well to ponder carefully as
to the advisability of undertaking the commitment to supervise.

34 By way of an aside on the topic of the Engineer's responsibility generally it might be inferred from decisions over the
years that the Engineer is assuming the role of ultimate
guarantor of the workmanship and financial stability of the
lowest tendering Contractor - this can only lead to ruin.

35 How does the insurance market respond in these circumstances?
In essence by offering Consulting Engineers professional
indemnity cover to protect them against claims made for neglect
error or omission resulting in death or injury to third parties
or damage to their property. Property extends to include such
matters as financial loss so that delays caused by the Engineer's
neglect error or omission are covered insofar as the claimant
can quantify them and attribute them. The policy does not sup-
plant Employers' Liability and Public Liability covers and
contains appropriate exclusions so that such claims fall to be
dealt with by the Underwriters of these contingencies.

36 In earlier years policies were written to cover claims
having their origin during a period of insurance, thus a claim
might be related back to a long-expired 'year of insurance';
nowadays policies cover claims made during the currency of the
policy and at each renewal the Engineer is required to declare
any circumstances which might give rise to a claim: we find that
many such circumstances may never develop into a claim, but that
sometimes a Writ is served on the last possible day to protect
the claimant's position should he decide to pursue the matter.
Hence such declarations need to be given after the most careful
review, and never lightly.

37 The reader will realise the significance of the reporting
date in an inflationary era when a level of cover which may have
seemed adequate at the time of an incident coming to light may
look less than adequate when it eventually comes to the time
for settlement.

38   Unlike a portfolio of fire insurance, a portfolio of professional indemnity insurance has a very long tail - that means
that it takes many years for the financial results of an underwriting year to become apparent.   As each fire insurance year is
closed losses have either occurred or not occurred and the ratio
of claims to premiums becomes clear so that appropriate action
can be taken; with a professional indemnity portfolio nothing
is ever entirely clear and with due regard to caution Underwriters used to write it only on the basis of an annual aggregate claims limit.   It is now offered on the basis of a limit
'each and every claim' for a modest premium enhancement and many
Engineers deem it prudent to effect some or indeed all of their
cover on this basis.

39   Public sector clients and not a few private sector clients
are increasingly making stipulations as to the nature and extent
of the professional indemnity coverage they require their Consultants to carry and whilst for many years such enquiries were
rejected as insulting and impudent - do you ask your surgeon for
details of his insurance coverage? - in times of eager work-search
and when the knowledge of the existence of professional indemnity
insurance has become widespread such a riposte bears little
weight.

40   However, it would be mistaken for Engineers or their clients
to assume that insurance can provide all the answers and this is
particularly important in the matter of guarantees and warranties
as to performance and fitness for purpose.   A manufacturer of
physical goods made from known components to known tolerances
for known purposes can reasonably predict a failure rate and offer
guarantees - a Consulting Engineer can and does undertake to
respect Codes and take due note of known data in his designs but
he can do no more than that and should decline to enter into
guarantees and warranties which are inappropriate.   His professional indemnity cover protects him against the consequences
of neglect error or omission, not against claims made under
guarantees.   It is important that all design professionals understand this vital fact.

41   The policy will commonly be extended to include Loss of
Documents and Libel & Slander: the potential for delay inherent
in a negligent loss of documents and the cost of reconstituting
freshly-taken original instructions require little imagination,
and a well-meant opinion as to the qualities or otherwise of a
manufacturer's products given in privileged circumstances from
professional to client but which reaches unintended ears or eyes
can lead to costly litigation and maybe an award of damages.

42   Many professional practices have considered limiting their
liability through the device of incorporation with limited
liability.   Whilst incorporation and the creation of a capital
structure which enables a founder to take his capital out of the
firm on his retirement may in some cases have its attractions,
and management and direction by a board of shareholding directors
may be less burdensome than the running of a partnership by a
process of consent, nevertheless the practice of a profession
behind limited liability has not proved universally acceptable

in these Islands nor in those territories with which we share
our mores and values. For a period after incorporation it may
be possible to practise as an unlimited company with restricted
shareholding but as the shareholding becomes dissipated more
widely through deaths the pressure to limit liability inevitably
mounts and limited liability in professional practice is bound
to become as transparent to the Courts as it is becoming in conventional trade. Once individuals are joined in a Writ they
become as vulnerable as partners in a conventional practice and
it is commonplace for limited liability companies operating in
professional fields to protect their professional liability
risks through insurance.

43 The selection of limits of indemnity and of uninsured
'excesses' borne by the practice cannot be subject to hard and
fast rules except to the extent that obligations may be imposed
by clients. By the application of such rules the small firm
which undertakes a limited number of highly significant engagements might appear to be over-insured whilst the large firm
which undertakes smaller engagements in considerable volume
might seem to be over-insured. Each firm is individual and it
is up to the Broker to give individual advice bearing in mind
the fee income, the nature of the engagements, the class of work,
the profitability and the wealth of the partners, the breadth or
narrowness of the exposure to risk, the claims experience, the
load of past work and the probability of future work - all of
these against a background of clients whose continued workflow
may be crucial and who may be obligated to insist upon the
application of rules of thumb.

44 From an insurance point of view supervision is an area of
claims of increasing significance as a comparison of the two
reviews I have mentioned will reveal. A fulsome check of the
methods employed in individual offices is well merited both now
and as a matter of continuing review.

Discussion on Papers 3–6

MR J. WASILEWSKI, Associate, Harris & Sutherland, London

In advising a client of the need for site supervision, a consulting engineer often has to go to some lengths to justify the need for such supervision. How can we, on the one hand, explain the need for continuous qualified supervision while, on the other hand, not imply that this will ensure that nothing will go wrong? In the ensuing discussions, the client will often ask 'what more am I getting for this supervision cost, if I am not getting an assurance of there being no problems?' What is he getting?

MR T. W. WEDDELL

The need for adequate supervision is best explained by pointing out the risks if inadequate workmanship is not identified at the time of construction. There are examples of failures reported from time to time in the technical press which may be cited to support the need for adequate supervision (both quality and quantity).

The supervisor is never in a position in which he can guarantee workmanship since it is the Contractor who carries out the work. However, increased supervision must normally reduce the risk of things going wrong.

The final question refers to the client's return for increased supervision costs. The benefits he gains include

(a)   reduced risk of delayed completion (for which he may not be adequately reimbursed by liquidated damages)
(b)   increased safety (failures resulting in injury or damage normally result in adverse publicity)
(c)   reduced risk of remedial works etc. after the limitation period, i.e. the period when the Contractor can be held liable
(d)   reduced maintenance costs
(e)   longer life.

MR E. M. O'LEARY, Partner, Veryard & Partners, Cardiff

In dealing with the various standard conditions of engagement Mr Weddell again raises the question of the distinction between 'supervision' and inspection. This matter was raised in the earlier papers but the distinction still eludes us.

I believe that the real answer lies in the act. Supervision is by definition overseeing. It is watching over the work in progress and can only be carried out by personnel on site, both those of the Engineer/Architect or those of the Contractor. Inspection, however, is examining and approving or otherwise work or work elements completed. It can be carried out by Visiting Engineers or Architects.

This can be clearly inferred from RIBA 82 and is, I believe, intended in ACE 2, so why not say so and emphasize that the duties of the consultant include inspection by the consultant and supervision by the Engineer's Representative (or Resident Engineer)?

MR J. C. FERGUSSON, London Transport Executive, London

Are the normal conditions of employment between an employer and an employee sufficient where a public authority's (etc.) own engineer is responsible for design and supervision, or should something resembling the ACE Conditions of Engagement be drawn up?

Mr Weddell: do you have any comments on the circumstances adopted on some smaller contracts where the Employer and the Engineer are the same person?

MR T. W. WEDDELL

I believe that the normal conditions of employment are adequate and that conditions resembling the ACE Conditions of Engagement are unnecessary and may be undesirable. The normal standard of care in each case is that of the professional man, i.e. reasonable skill, care and diligence. The few reported cases of employers suing their employees for breach of their contracts of employment or for negligence relate only to very special circumstances.

Regarding the final question, in my experience there have been few instances where the Employer and the Engineer are the same person. The Employer is normally a government department, local authority, a corporation or a company. The Engineer is normally a particular person or group of persons such as a partnership. The important point is that a clear distinction must be maintained between the Engineer and the Employer even if the Engineer is an employee of the Employer. The Engineer must rigorously maintain his independence, and if necessary explain his duty to do so, to his employer. He must

resist any attempt to interfere with his independent role –
see ICE Guidance Note 2A.

MR J. C. FERGUSSON, London Transport Executive, London

What are the disadvantages of management contracts?
    'It is pointless for consultants to duplicate the Management
Contractor's responsibilities for site supervision', says Mr
Cottam. Do the Engineer and Resident Engineer have no role
and responsibilities with regard to site supervision in a
management contract?
    Indeed, can the Management Contractor be the Engineer as
stated in Mr Deuce's paper?
    My employer is currently embarking on several management
contracts which embody adapted versions of the ICE conditions,
since it is noted there is no standard form for an ICE-based
management contract. One proposal is for the Management
Contractor to be defined as the Employer, the principal
construction sub-contractor the Contractor and the employer's
engineer still being the Engineer. Have you any comments on
this?
    Is it really possible for a client's Engineer to avoid all
responsibilities and legal liability for negligence arising
from a defect in construction simply by setting up a
management contract? Consider the situation where the
client's Engineer has responsibility for the security and
maintenance of the works after the end of the maintenance
period.
    What would be the situation if both the Management
Contractor and the construction sub-contractor have ceased to
exist. Could the Engineer then become liable for negligence
appearing in a subsequent defect etc?

MR G. D. G. COTTAM

Unfortunately the questioner has clearly failed to grasp the
role of the Management Contractor. The Management Contractor
is part of the professional team working like other members
for a fee, and his responsibility is for both the design and
the supervision of the execution of the work; there is
therefore no role for another Engineer or Resident Engineer in
addition to the Management Contractor's staff. It follows
that the Management Contractor is the Engineer under the
construction contracts and the client's Engineer adopts the
unaccustomed role of being the client. When adapting the ICE
conditions for a management contract it must be clear that we
are considering the Management Contractor's contract with the
Employer or the Construction Contractor's contract with the
Management Contractor. If under the construction contract the
Engineer is to be the employer's Engineer, then the whole
point of the Management Contractor's role is missed and what

we are then talking about is a project manager being
appointed, and not a Management Contractor.

If the Management Contractor is appointed to be responsible
for the design, then the client's Engineer contracts out of
design liability provided that he does not undertake any
design himself; however, in his role as the client, he cannot
contract out of the normal liabilities of a client under a
construction contract.

After the completion of the maintenance period there is no
difference in liability for the security and maintenance of
the works whether a management contract or a normal ICE
contract had been used for the construction. The question of
liabilities is decided by the Contract, together with who pays
in the event of a claim. However, if we are considering who
pays if either the management contract, or a sub-contractor
becomes bankrupt, then we are not dealing with contractual
liabilities but who pays. It is therefore a question of risk.
The balance of risk for the client must be in favour of the
management contract since more of the liability is accepted by
the Management Contractor than by a Contractor under the ICE
conditions.

MR G. M. HANNAH, Partner, Hannah, Reed & Associates, Cambridge

An additional weakness to those listed by Mr Cottam would be
the lack of independence of certain Management Contractors,
especially if the Management Contractor is part of a
disreputable conglomerate and undergoes certain pressures on
the activities and decisions which are not applicable to the
independent consulting engineer.

MR J. DALLAWAY, Supervision Manager, Ove Arup Partnership,
London

Speaking as a member of a firm which has maintained a high
profile in the supervision of the work for which it is
responsible we have run into increasing difficulty on two main
fronts both of which have been referred to previously.

One is the level of supervision which a client will pay for.
We have to take a very forward position with clients to obtain
the level of supervision appropriate. We do not always
achieve the level we would wish. We start therefore with our
hand tied behind our back. Letters on file may help if the
recommendations have not been accepted and things go wrong in
the future.

Secondly, and to some extent in contrast with what I have
already said, a high profile on site attracts
responsibilities: we find ourselves providing effective
quality control of the works and, should there be problems in
the future, we may be much more exposed as a consequence of
the level of input - albeit the contractual responsibility for

performing the work properly is the Contractor's.

So for either or both of these reasons, the consultant is likely to look for some other way to ensure that the work is done correctly. He may look towards the recent moves encouraged by government and given shape in BS 5750 for quality assurance and quality control. This sets out guidelines for the establishment of systems designed to ensure quality by the producer or manufacturer who in our case is the Contractor, his sub-contractors and suppliers.

A significant feature of these guidelines is that those responsible for the quality control should have this as their unique function.

We have already seen the introduction of quality assurance systems into contracts in the nuclear construction field. We have been involved with them in some of our work overseas implemented at the instigation of the client. I think that we shall begin to see many more contracts placed when the onus of providing effective quality control is placed on the Contractor.

Some contractors appear to accept that this will be so, and indeed may consider offering such a service as an 'optional extra'. Should they not be doing it anyway?

This brings me on to Mr Cottam's paper and contribution. Management Contractors tend to make a sales pitch which includes their expertise in quality control. Mr Cottam has said that they should exercise supervision and quality control as an irreducible minimum. He obviously thinks that it is important.

We have much experience of management contracting: we could be said to have written the book or, at least, quite a bit of it.

Our experience with the Management Contractors has in most cases been satisfactory. They have been much less successful as quality controllers. We often find ourselves having to supplement their activities, or lack of them, in this connection, by our own efforts.

The problems arise for two main reasons. Management Contractors' staff have, in most cases come from a conventional contracting background. They are not tuned into looking for quality as a prime requirement. Furthermore the range of duties given to the members of staff with responsibility for quality control will include activities which are more obviously progress related, and these usually assume priority: quality control suffers.

This situation is magnified in one of Mr Cottam's suggestions that Management Contractors work not in a quasi-professional role only, receiving a simple percentage fee for their services (a situation which we prefer) but in a target cost framework. This may mean that they have a financial incentive to finish the job as rapidly as possible. Is not this objective likely to conflict with the responsibility for quality control?

I welcome Mr Cottam's comments. Furthermore, and taking up

a point made in the discussion of his paper, the suggestion that management contracts may be more expensive than conventional contracts has been made and this may be so, but we have to realize what is gained. A management contract should allow you to start a contract, and finish it, earlier than if a conventional contract is adopted. An employer can make enormous savings in interest charges and can begin to obtain a return on his investment much earlier than would be the case with a conventional contract. These amounts may be very much greater than any additional construction cost that may have arisen from a management contract.

MR R. FREER, Engineer, Pencol Engineering Consultants, London

Mr Cottam has described some of the problems of management contracting including the possibility that the client bears the greater part of the risk. Will the client be satisfied with coping with this risk if he knows that he is adequately covered by insurance?

Major recent structures such as the Humber Bridge and the Thames Barrier have overrun cost and twice to an extent which would embarass a private client. Would a method of management contracting for such prestigious projects provide greater surity that they would be completed on time and on cost?

DR N. M. L. BARNES, Martin Barnes & Partners, Stockport

Mr Cottam was wrong on two points: (a) management contracting does not place all the risk on the client - most of the risk is carried, as conventionally, by the sub-contractors; (b) management contracting does not necessarily add a tier of management - only for work which a main contractor would normally do himself (which is not much) - and anyway, if the management contracting staff are not achieving more than they cost, you should not be doing it.

MR J. WASILEWSKI, Associate, Harris & Sutherland, London

A project has many cost elements, of which the construction cost is only one and the design cost is another. In management contracting both these costs are under a single head - but what of the other costs: how can a 'buyer/client' hope to retain any involvement in the apportionment of project cost elements (a) maintenance costs, (b) running costs and (c) risk cost, which is a function of the design principles, factors of safety, return periods etc., in a balance which suits him?

MR G. D. G. COTTAM

The Management Contractor operates under a brief prepared by
the client. It is essential that this brief be carefully
controlled since it defines the client's requirements in
detail. One method for the client to control the cost limits
referred to is by employing a consulting engineer to draw up
the brief to make certain that the parameters required for
maintenance and running costs are clearly set out. Each of
the briefs will be in the form of a performance specification;
this should cover adequately all the cost items.

It is always important when discussing design details to
differentiate between those items which are factual and those
which are personal prejudice. The former can be defined, the
latter, it must be accepted, are not going to be met under a
management-type contract.

MR M. J. BRETON, Sir Robert McAlpine & Sons Ltd, London

Dr Barnes: what are your views on how one can overcome the
problem for a contractor to keep within the programme time
when it is common for the supply of information from the
consultants to be outside the time shown on the programme?

DR N. M. L. BARNES

This is a problem which occurs with surprising frequency. I
do not believe that there is a simple way of avoiding the
problem. It can be mitigated by producing a very
comprehensive schedule of information requirements with the
clause 14 programme submission. The schedule should be
realistic in the sense that it should not ask for information
too far ahead of the real need and it should also leave the
consultants in no doubt at all about exactly what information
is required. It is not enough merely to put a mark on the bar
chart ahead of each bar to represent when the relevant
information is required.

MR E. P. MALONEY, Brian Colquhoun & Partners, Bedford

Looking for a means of tightening up the control of programme
time I have had experience overseas of a turnkey project which
had conditions applied to it whereby stage payments were
strictly tied to section completions. Speaking from the
Contractor's viewpoint I can vouch for the pressure that this
put on us to achieve our targets - especially to finish
sections.

Dr Barnes: what is your opinion of this method of control
of timing of the project?

DR N. M. L. BARNES

I hope that my paper conveys my general view that attention to
the timing of construction work needs to be strengthened and
that any devices leading in this direction are probably worth
using. I am also keen on relating stage payments to
completion of sections of the work or to completion of
activities shown on contract programmes. This not only
encourages the Contractor to complete, it also reduces the
administrative load in preparing valuations. There is a
problem, however, in that many activities or sections of the
work are not 100% complete until practical completion or
indeed until the end of the maintenance period. Where one
uses stage payments it is consequently important to be
prepared to pay for effective completion of a stage, not to
demand 100% completion.

MR I. B. WEBB, Planning Engineer, Wimpey International Ltd,
Iver Heath

I am always pleased to see papers concerned with the subject
of time in construction projects as I feel the value of time
is not well understood by some engineers.
   Referring to the appendix attached to the paper, Dr Barnes,
do you think that clients will be able to award contracts to
contractors whose price is not the lowest if the tender
programme demonstrates a favourable cash flow for the client?
Also do you think that the extra overheads involved in
providing the information required in the appendix justifies
the benefits obtained?

DR N. M. L. BARNES

I see no problem about awarding contracts to contractors whose
price is not the lowest but whose cash flow is most favourable
for the client, provided that the intention of assessing
tenders in this way is made clear to tenderers in the
invitation documents. It is essential that contractors should
understand how their tenders will be compared if it is other
than on the lowest price, and in this connection the discount
rate which the client proposes to use for comparison has to be
stated.
   I am not in any doubt that the extra overheads involved in
providing the information outlined in the appendix to my paper
are justified by the benefits to be obtained. There is a
negligible additional overhead cost for a contractor who is
planning his work effectively and maintaining basic time
control information. Providing the information to the
Engineer creates very little further cost and ensures that
time control methods can be handled effectively at the
contractual interface.

MR A. SANDBERG, Senior Partner, Messrs Sandberg, London

I am very concerned about the effects of 'knock-on' liability.
I have recently met a consulting engineer who was defending 34
architects against negligence. He said that when the
Contractor was still in existence the liability of the
Architect was normally of the order of 15%, but where the
Contractor had gone into liquidation the Architect was
potentially 100% liable and, as Mr Griffiths has pointed out,
this might be for an extremely long period.

This in effect means that, when Mr Griffiths is asked by a
professional architect or engineer for his professional
indemnity policy, he is not mainly being asked for insurance
against professional negligence, but an insurance against his
Contractor going into liquidation for an indeterminate period
in the future. The Association of Consulting Engineers has
written to the Law Reform Committee on this point, who replied
to the effect that they could see that it was a valid point,
but one which they thought was not covered by their present
somewhat limited terms of reference.

I have subsequently spoken to the Law Reform Committee, who
said that the point was valid for discussion but should be
raised as a new issue with the Lord Chancellor, and it was
hoped that it might be possible to do this, preferably in
conjunction with the Architects, Quantity Surveyors and
Contractors who were similarly affected.

A solicitor has advised me that on a recent case he asked
the judge if he would apportion responsibility in addition to
liability, but the judge refused to do so.

I have discussed the problem of 'knock-on' liabilities with
two judges, both of whom stated that the law was exceedingly
unfair in this particular matter, but there was nothing that
they, as judges, could do other than to act on the law as it
now stood. It is up to us to set about changing the law,
which ties in with the proposed approach to the Lord
Chancellor.

Other solutions might include enforceable clauses limiting
liability although it seems generally agreed that these are of
doubtful standing in the courts, more particularly when a
third party is involved. I have also pursued the merits of
decennial insurance with one firm of insurance brokers, who
charge a premium to the client, to guarantee the building
against defects for ten years. They explained, however, that
they repossessed their money by subrogation from the
professionals and contractors in the normal way, except that
they were possibly rather better at this particular function
through practice than an individual client might be.

MR P. J. CUNLIFFE, Principal Assistant Engineer, Bury
Metropolitan Borough Council, Manchester

Notwithstanding Mr Griffiths' assurance that insurers regard supervision seriously and take supervision into account when assessing claims, I wonder whether they ever see any further than ICE clause 22(1)(b)(iv)?

Whenever a third-party claim arises for damage occurring in the vicinity of a contract, it is my experience that insurers will do little more than say that it is 'the unavoidable result of the construction of the works'.

If insurers are indeed regarding supervision in its wider implications then surely it should not need an engineer's decision that clause 22(1)(b)(iv) does not apply before insurers consider the detailed third-party claims and arrive at settlements.

MR K. E. O. GRIFFITHS

The insurance provided against the Contractor's liabilities is no wider than the liabilities imposed on the Contractor. Under clause 22(1)(b)(iv) the Contractor is not liable for inevitable damage. It seems entirely reasonable for his insurer to start negotiations from the proposition that damage to adjacent property was inevitable. The Insured would not wish the Insurer to pay out unnecessary claims — it would merely mean that his future premium rates would be increased.

DR N. M. L. BARNES, Martin Barnes & Partners, Stockport

Is not the state of never-ending liability the best argument available for consultants to operate as limited liability companies?

MR K. E. O. GRIFFITHS

Operating through a company, whether limited or unlimited, enables a practitioner to put an end to the liabilities arising from his practice other, as I understand it, than those liabilities which flow from his own personal negligence. I agree that this is an advantage, but it is not perhaps an overwhelming advantage. Lawyers have not yet thought it necessary to permit limited liability practice in either branch of the law.

It is worth remembering that operation as a limited liability company can affect other matters as well as liability.

7 The role of the Engineer

T. L. G. DEUCE, FEng, FICE, FIStructE, FIHT, Deputy Engineering Director, British
Airports Authority, Gatwick

SYNOPSIS. Based upon the author's experience of performing the
role of Engineer and of employing Engineers, the paper attempts
to set the Engineer's unique role in the context of the need
for him to exercise his role in person, to be impartial, to
take advice, to guide his staff and to work with the contractor
in a spirit of co-operation. The influences of claims and
variations are highlighted as is the importance of keeping the
employer informed and of listening to all points of view before
reaching decisions.

INTRODUCTION
The legal implications and obligations of the Engineer under
the contract have been covered in the earlier papers. In this
series, on supervision in practice, other authors are contributing on the roles of the Engineer's Representative, the
Contractor and the Site Agent. This paper is thus only
concerned with the role which the Engineer himself fulfills.
It is written with reference to the terms of the 5th Edition of
the ICE Form but many of the views expressed apply equally to
other forms.

THE ENGINEER
The person who is named as Engineer in the Contract documents
has an obligation to discharge that function personally. This
may seem straight-forward and obvious but it is one of the
Engineer's primary obligations and deserves to be clearly
stated and equally clearly understood. It is directly because
this is not always the case in practice that a number of
contracts encounter difficulty. It must be presupposed that it
was the intention of the Employer (the supposed draftsman of
the contract) that the Engineer was chosen with care.

All too often the head of an organisation is named as Engineer
but leaves the running of the contract to the resident engineer
and expects his deputy to deal with any problems and administer
the contract in the Engineer's name. More than once I have
come across contracts in which disputes have escalated to the
arbitration stage and found that the Engineer knew next to
nothing about them. When I, on behalf of the sponsoring
authority, asked the Engineer to explain the circumstances his

deputy would be sent instead. Upon later confronting the Engineer with his obligations and probing his disinterest the typical reply has been that he, the named Engineer, is far too busy to deal with details of that sort and has always left the running of contracts to his deputy. Such titular Engineers are failing in their duty to their Employer, to the Contractor and to the profession and are probably acting fraudulently by so doing. If they are too busy to discharge their obligations they should acknowledge the fact and arrange for their deputy, or some other such person with adequate experience, to fill the role of Engineer. I know of several organisations in which this is done. Alternatively it is fully open to the Employer to appoint an agent or a consultant or a management contractor to be the Engineer. The important thing is that the person appointed has the time and experience to perform the role properly. Everyone, including the Contractor, then knows where they stand. If arrangements can be made for the roles of Employer and Engineer to be separated and not to be performed by the same person that is obviously desirable.

The Engineer is bound by the provisions of the Contract to inform the Contractor of any powers which he has delegated and is barred from delegating his more important powers. The Contractor is, therefore, entitled to expect that the person named as the Engineer will himself deal with all the matters which are not delegated. Fortunately for Engineers who are not discharging their obligations properly the Contractor is seldom likely to be able to prove the matter. Were he able to do so he would be in a strong position to declare the Contract at large through breach by the Employer due to the Engineer's failure to act in accordance with the Contract.

IMPARTIALITY

The Engineer has a duty to act impartially. This is not expressly written but through the provisions of the contract this must clearly be the understanding of the parties. It is probably not going too far to say that a contract is liable to stand or fall on the Engineer's impartiality. It is the principal guarantee both parties have that the Works will be constructed on the agreed basis and that neither will incur costs for which, under the conditions, they are not liable. If the Engineer were to be shown to be partial toward the Employer, the Contractor would be bound to challenge all his decisions and, if he could prove the matter, would again probably have grounds for breach of Contract by the Employer. Irrespective of an Engineer's own short-comings, any attempt to coerce an Engineer away from a strictly impartial position by either party is, of course, a very grave matter. The Engineer has a clear responsibility to listen to all points of view expressed by either of the parties before reaching decisions and the clear distinction between coercion and trying to influence an Engineer's decision by force of argument and fact must there-fore be clearly understood.

90

The Engineer is required by many provisions in the contract to
decide what is reasonable in the relevant circumstances and to
apportion responsibility for risks and costs between the parties
in accordance with the provisions of the Contract. Clearly the
need for him to do so impartially requires that he acts fairly
but nowhere is he expressly required to be fair. He is bound
to interpret the Contract as it is written, even if it is unfair
as he has no power to substitute his own views or to change the
provisions of the Contract. Many of his decisions may appear
to either of the parties to be positively unfair in some
circumstances. This is not to say that the Engineer is barred
from making representations to either party on behalf of the
other to seek a mutual agreement to vary the provisions of the
Contract or to make some ex-gratia allowance or payment in
extenuating circumstances that were clearly beyond the contem-
plation of the parties at the time the contract was entered
into.

It is often asserted that Engineers who are employees of the
Employer cannot be truly impartial as their living depends upon
their allegiance to the Employer and that only consulting
engineers can perform a truly independant and impartial
function. I naturally dispute this, based not only on my own
direct experience but also on my experience of employing agent
authorities. I believe arguments of this sort profit us
little if we are worthy of being chartered engineers but I make
the point here to emphasise my belief that the servant of an
Employer is infact in a very strong position against the
possibility of victimisation by his employer, whereas a
consultant's right to a future commission is not at all
assured.

CONSULTATION
Reference has already been made to the Engineer's general duty
to listen to the points of view of both parties before coming
to decisions. However, few contracts would make any progress
if the Engineer went around consulting everyone before he
decided anything. What he must do is to ensure that the
Employer is kept fully informed about the progress of the
contract, of any significant difficulties that have arisen and
of any other matter which could be of consequence to him. He
should also ensure that all variation orders, certificates and
important letters are copied to the Employer. In all these
matters the Engineer should be guided by the fact that the
Contractor, being much closer to the job, will know all that is
going on and will be in a position to make representations on
any matter which concerns him whereas the Employer will
generally only be in such a position if the Engineer keeps him
fully informed.

In addition to his duty to listen to the parties the Engineer
should not shrink from seeking specialist advice or opinion
should the need arise. On a point of law an opinion from
Leading Counsel can do much to quell arguements over the

Engineer's interpretation of the contract. However, the crucial point is that having taken advice and having listened to arguments from either or both parties the Engineer must make up his own mind and make his own decision without fear or favour. It is always good practice to make a written note of the reasoning behind a decision. This is particularly so if an Engineer has occasion to rule contrary to expert advice. Not only will such a note be an aid to memory if the decision is subsequently challenged, but the discipline of committing an argument to paper often helps to clarify the issues.

DELEGATION

The Engineer is responsible for the actions of his staff and should, therefore, brief them carefully as to their powers and responsibilities. Even if the Engineer's Representative has none of the Engineer's powers delegated to him under the contract, if he is resident on site he will be acting as the Engineer's eyes and ears and must be guided as to what he is to do about what he sees and hears. Much more commonly he will have specific powers delegated to him by the Engineer and under the terms of the contract these will also have been notified to the Contractor. In this case the RE will in addition need to be given clear guidance on how to interpret these powers, how frequently and in what form he is to report to the Engineer and in which circumstances he is to call in the Engineer. He will also need to be told of any financial limits the Engineer may wish to set upon his delegated powers together with a range of administrative details.

Most Engineers will give their staff guidance along the lines that if anything unusual or untoward happens upon the site they are to be told immediately and that if they later discover anything of importance which comes as a surprise to them the RE will be judged to have failed in his duty to keep the Engineer informed. I am often well content to let an RE attempt to solve a problem provided that I have been told that a problem exists and have thus been given the opportunity to offer advice or alternatively of stepping in if I judge the situation so warrants. What an RE must always remember is that regardless of the power delegated to him he is exercising that power with the authority of the Engineer who still remains fully responsible for the conduct of the contract. This, of course, applies equally to all members of the Engineer's staff.

It is also important for the Engineer's staff to realise that they are directly responsible to the Engineer alone and that they may not accept any instructions concerning the conduct of the contract from anybody else without the Engineer's express agreement. This often has to be relied upon to deter the introduction of "improvements" by designers and clients without the Engineer's knowledge or agreement and without the introducers having a clear understanding of the possible consequences upon the Contract.

RELATIONSHIPS

The relationship which exists between an Engineer and his staff
has an important influence on the smooth running of a contract.
If it is poor it will inhibit the success of a contract but if
it is good the teamwork which will stem from it will enable
many problems to be solved with ease.

The resident engineer must be encouraged to play a positive
role and employ skill and energy in trouble-shooting and
looking ahead. If he is good at his job he will not only serve
the Engineer well, he will also be an asset to the Employer and
to the Contractor alike. The RE's relationship with the
Contractor's Agent and his staff is also of great importance.
I have in the past removed a resident engineer from a site when
I judged that he was probably the source of friction. I took
the precaution of telling the Contractor that I would require
him to remove his Agent from the site if the friction continued
thereafter!

I believe there is much which the Engineer can and should do to
foster good relations with the contractor and that it is a very
important part of his role to maintain lines of communication
with the Contractor's senior staff. Not only will this enable
him to express concern in a helpful way before matters come to
a head, but it will also help to foster a spirit of co-operation and provide a hot-line in case of need. I take the
view that without in any way detracting from the Employer's
interests much can be gained to the mutual benefit of both the
parties if the Engineer and the Contractor's senior staff have
open lines of communication throughout a contract.

From day one the site staff on both sides should start to
compile the final measurement and thus aim to produce the final
account very shortly after the Certificate of Completion has
been given. This practice is much more universally adopted now
than it was a few years ago when the final accounts for a
significant number of contracts around the country were outstanding four and five years after completion. This was a
deplorable situation which was in nobody's interest and could
often be traced not only to a lack of co-operation but also to
poor management.

Completion of a contract within an agreed time scale is one of
the Contractor's primary obligations and trying to ensure that
it is complied with is one of the Engineer's principal
responsibilities and preoccupations. It is right that this
should be the case but if a spirit of co-operation does not
exist between the Engineer and the Contractor this preoccu-
pation can be irksome and if pursued insensitively will soon
result in bad feeling. Nevertheless the Engineer must not
shirk his responsibility and if a contract is running behind
programme he must do all in his power to analyse the cause and
bring it to the Contractor's attention in a helpful way before
he has to bring the full weight of his powers under the contract
to bear.

93

VARIATIONS

The ability to introduce variations into civil engineering contracts can be a valuable facility but it is one which is all too often abused and relied upon to make up for deficiencies in the design. Any Engineer or Employer who introduces variations other than to solve unexpected problems is asking for trouble and generally gets it. Variations all too often result in a justification for an extension of time and increases in cost which might well have been avoided had the work been included in the tender documents. The fact that the provision exists and can easily be used is very tempting but it is a temptation which should be resisted with determination and Engineers should be very clear in advising their Employers as to the consequences of introducing them.

The ICE 5th Edition lays down clear rules about the circumstances which may entitle a Contractor to an extension of time and dictates the action that the Engineer should take. Notwithstanding that, Engineers tend to be reluctant to grant extensions at the time the circumstances become clear and seem to prefer to put off making a decision, presumably in some forlorn hope that the circumstances will go away. This is thoroughly bad practice which is in nobody's interest and often rebounds against the Employer, the one whose interest such Engineers presumably think they are safeguarding.

CLAIMS

No paper on the Engineer's role would seem to be complete without some reference to claims. I include reference to them with reluctance as they have come to be regarded with some distaste due to the way in which some contractors seek to exploit them at every vestige of an opportunity and to invent opportunities where none exist. These are strong words but such attitudes regrettably do exist and in my opinion are harmful to the industry. If genuine grounds for a claim exist then the Contractor is entitled to have them fully investigated and settled properly and it is the Engineer's duty to do so impartially. It is, however, equally his duty to reject unjustified claims which seem to be spawned by some Contractors in the hope that they might get something for their trouble if they try it on. Little do they realise the distaste this causes and the consequent harm this does them when tender lists are being drawn up. The avoidance of variations and an insistence upon comprehensive contract documents at the time of tender are the best ways of avoiding claims.

OTHER PROFESSIONS

Quantity surveyors have an important role to play in the service of the Engineer. Their professional skill and experience can be of considerable value in helping the Engineer ensure the completeness and adequacy of tender documents. Likewise in admeasurement and valuation during the currency of a contract they can perform a valuable service. However, they in common with other professional advisers such

94

as accountants and lawyers must not loose sight of the fact
that no matter how good and skilled they are their duty is to
serve the Engineer who alone must make the decisions and take
full responsibility for all that they do on his behalf.

In conclusion let it be said that the Engineer's role in
practice is to act as the agent of the Employer, to supervise
the construction of the Works, to ensure that the Contractor
constructs them in accordance with the Contract, to make
decisions on the allocation to the parties of responsibility
for risks and costs, to determine the time within which the
Works are to be constructed and, in the words of the ICE
Conditions of Contract Standing Joint Committee, "in all
respects to act within the terms of the contract, impartially,
honestly and with professional integrity towards both the
parties to the contract".

All opinions expressed in this paper are those of the author
and are in no way to be interpreted as being agreed to by the
British Airports Authority.

8 The role of the Engineer's Representative

J. R. SWEETAPPLE, FICE, Partner, Rendel Palmer Tritton, London

SYNOPSIS.   Responsibilities and powers of the Engineer's Representative are discussed followed by consideration of his duties in respect of the contract programme and recording and reporting progress. Reference is made to site meetings and inspections and the relationship between the Engineer's Representative and the Contractor's Agent.   Thereafter, the remaining more important of the Engineer's Representative's duties throughout a contract are noted and commented upon. Brief descriptions of the charts and other records to be kept by the Engineer's Representative are included in the text; the provision of examples is not considered necessary since what is recommended is uncomplicated and the principles should be well known to readers of this paper.

1.   In discussing the role of the Engineer's Representative frequent reference has to be made to the ICE Conditions of Contract. All clause numbers quoted herein are those in the ICE Conditions of Contract - Fifth Edition. Whilst, in a short paper, it is not possible to cover every aspect of an Engineer's Representative's duties, an attempt has been made to include the more important matters relating to his role applicable to an admeasurement type of Contract.

DEFINITION
2.   Under the ICE Conditions of Contract "Engineer's Representative" means a person being the resident engineer or assistant of the Engineer or clerk of works appointed from time to time by the Employer or the Engineer.   The Engineer's Representative, or ER, as he will be called hereafter, whether he is appointed by the Employer or the Engineer is responsible to and only to the Engineer.

BASIC RESPONSIBILITIES
3.   The ER's responsibilities in a way mirror the Engineer's basic responsibilities during the construction stage of a project, which are to ensure that the work is carried out in accordance with the contract, for the right price and within the stipulated time. In all his dealings the ER he must act fairly, keeping an even balance between the interests of the Employer and the interests of the Contractor. An ER must not enter upon his duties convinced that the

Contractor cannot be trusted. The Contractor's Agent will probably be as or more experienced than the ER, as technically qualified and as professionally minded as he is. Nevertheless, a good ER must fearlessly exercise his authority to impress upon the Contractor that work inferior to the standard required by the Contract will not be accepted. It is particularly important, at the outset, to get this point across to the Contractor.

NO POWER TO RELIEVE CONTRACTOR OF OBLIGATIONS

4.   The ER has no power to relieve the Contractor of any of his obligations under the contract. It is no part of the ER's duties to suggest or accept any alternative to the requirements laid down or to intervene in any way in the Contractor's manner of organising or carrying out the works. The ICE Conditions of Contract make it absolutely clear that the Contractor and only the Contractor is responsible for the adequacy, stability and safety of all operations on site and methods of construction (other than temporary works designed by the Engineer).

5.   When the Engineer or ER, under powers delegated to him, calls for details of the Contractor's proposals under Clause 14(3), or gives his consent to those proposals under Clause 14(4), it is in respect only of whether the Contractor's methods will enable work to be constructed in accordance with the drawings and specification, without detriment to the permanent works when completed. It is not the responsibility of the ER to ensure that the Contractor's proposals meet safety criteria. This does not mean that the Engineer or ER should not take all appropriate steps, when consenting to proposals under Clause 14(4), to satisfy himself on aspects of safety of the temporary and permanent works during all stages of the operations. Further, if the ER sees a potentially dangerous situation developing on the site, he should warn the Contractor. Whilst, at this stage, this is really a moral issue rather than a duty under the contract, the ER would, if the situation demanded, exercise powers delegated to him under Clause 40.

6.   The Contractor is responsible, under Clause 19(1), for having full regard to the safety of all persons on the site and for maintaining the site and the works (except parts completed and occupied by the Employer) in an orderly state appropriate to the avoidance of damage to personnel. Lights, guards, fencing, warning signs and watchmen must be provided by the Contractor when or where necessary or required by the Engineer (or ER since authority is invariably delegated in the case of this clause) or by any competent statutory or other authority for the protection of the works or for the safety and convenience of the public. The fact that the contract states that the ER may require the Contractor to provide safety measures does not relieve the Contractor of responsibility for safety and security or his obligations to satisfy the safety requirements of competent statutory or other authorities. Having said this, the ER and his staff should, at all times, be alert as to the safety requirements throughout the site and on the works and should draw the Contractor's attention immediately, in writing, to any safety or security measures requiring attention.

CONTRACT DOCUMENTS TO BE STUDIED

7.   The first duty of the ER, on appointment, is to make a thorough study of the Contract i.e. the Drawings, Specification, Bills of Quantities, Conditions of Contract and Special Conditions. Special Conditions are amendments and additions to the ICE Conditions of Contract applicable to a particular project. Since it is very easy to refer to the Conditions of Contract and to overlook an amendment or addition in the Special Conditions, a bit of good advice to any ER is to carefully cross reference the Conditions of Contract with the Special Conditions, so that reference to the Conditions of Contract immediately alerts the reader to an amendment or addition contained in the Special Conditions.

8.   Usually the Engineer appointed for the construction stage of a project will have been responsible for the preparation of the tender documents. In such circumstances the Engineer will have an intimate knowledge of the design, specification and billing; however, even if this is the case and more particularly if it is not, a good ER will study drawings, specification and bills of quantities, in detail, so that he can refer annomalies or apparent omissions to the Engineer, at an early stage, in advance of questions being raised by the Contractor. Very often, if an ambiguity or discrepancy in the several documents forming the contract has been brought to the notice of the Engineer at an early stage, something can be done to mitigate adverse effects which may be suffered by the Employer. Ambiguities or discrepancies discovered by the Contractor and notified at a late stage under Clause 5 often lead to delay and extra cost which might have been avoided or minimised.

DELEGATED POWERS

9.   Where powers or authorities have been delegated to the ER by the Contract itself or by a separate delegation from the Engineer, he must study the appropriate clauses carefully and understand fully the responsibilities delegated to him. The Engineer delegates powers to the ER in accordance with Clause 2(3); such delegation must be in writing and must be copied to the Contractor. A delegation of powers by the Engineer to the ER is often worded "In the following clauses for ENGINEER read ENGINEER OR ENGINEER'S REPRESENTATIVE". Powers are delegated both in respect of clauses in the Conditions of Contract (including the Special Conditions) and the Specification. When initially studying the clauses under which powers have been delegated it is recommended that the ER should clearly indicate in, or against the relevant clauses, that powers have been delegated to him. It is suggested that the words ENGINEER'S REPRESENTATIVE should be underlined in red where powers are already delegated by the contract; elsewhere, when powers of the Engineer have been extended to the Engineer's Representative the words OR ENGINEER'S REPRESENTATIVE should be inserted in red.

10.   Time spent by the ER, at the earliest opportunity, in annotating and cross-referenceing his set of contract documents is time that could not be better spent.

11.   It is important to note that the ER has no authority to delegate any of the powers, which have been delegated to him, to his assistants. Under Clause 2(2), the Engineer or ER may appoint

persons to assist the ER in the exercise of his duties. The Contractor must be informed of the names and functions of such assistants. It is most important that the ER should lay down clearly the duties of each of his engineers, inspectors etc. and should agree, with the Contractor, standard procedures and standard forms for recording notification and acceptance of all things necessary to ensure that setting out, lines and levels, materials and workmanship are in accordance with the specification and drawings.

PROGRAMME AND PROGRESS

12.   Clause 14 requires the Contractor to submit a programme to the Engineer (or ER if powers under this clause have been delegated to him) within 21 days of the acceptance of the tender. There is usually a specification clause amplifying the requirements of Clause 14 and possibly extending the time for submission of the programme.

13.   Whether authority to approve the Contractor's programme lies with the Engineer or the ER, the latter should be given opportunity to study and discuss it with the Contractor's Agent before approval is given to the programme in its final and agreed form. It is very important that there should be an approved contract programme at the earliest possible date, against which progress can be monitored.   A practical type of programme for most civil engineering contracts is a simple bar chart. Actual progress can be recorded monthly, in a separate colour or type of line, below or above bars indicating the programme.

14.   At the start of a contract is is good practice for the ER to evaluate the Contractor's programme against the priced bills of quantities and to produce a cash flow curve. Against this curve actual values of work done can be plotted from monthly certificates of payment.

15.   The bar chart is very useful in identifying slippages in the various sections of work whilst the cash flow curve indicates, at a glance, any overall underspend and delay to the completion of the works as a whole.

16.   In addition to bar charts and progress curves, on a well run and documented job, progress drawings capable of being marked up to show the state of all major parts of the works will be maintained in the ER's office. Such drawings, which again should be marked up to show progress each month, are invaluable at progress meetings and for reference throughout a contract.

MATTERS AFFECTING PROGRESS

17.   Whilst the recording of actual progress is important, it is equally important that full and accurate records should be maintained of all matters affecting progress and the completion of the contract. A number of such records have to be submitted to the ER by the Contractor, in accordance with the requirements of the ICE Conditions of Contract and the specification. It is important for the ER to agree with the Contractor, before work on site commences, the form, content and the times for submission of such returns, which may include:

- Daily returns of numbers and categories of Contractor's and Sub-contractor's labour and details on work on which employed.
- Monthly returns of constructional plant and where employed including details of periods of breakdown and maintenance.
- Records of materials received on the site and materials used in the permanent works and for temporary work.
- Reports on accidents to personnel or to the temporary and permanent works.

18. Records of other things affecting progress of the work which should be kept by the ER, must be comprehensive and would include such matters as:

- Rainfall
- Wind direction and velocity
- Tide levels
- Sea conditions
- Flood levels
- Ground water levels

19. It is good practice for the ER to plot the continuous records of labour, plant, materials supply, site conditions etc. on charts to the same horizontal scale as the programme and progress bar diagrams and cash flow curves. These charts should be kept up-to-date and will permit direct comparison between progress and the things upon which progress depends; this is of particular assistance when considering applications for extension of contract time and can be an invaluable source of information in assessing the validity of Contractor's claims.

RATE OF PROGRESS

20. Whilst the Contractor's programme and the recording of progress have been referred to previously, it is also necssary to consider what action can be taken by the Engineer or ER should the rate of progress fall behind that required by the contract. Under Clause 14(2), should it appear that actual progress does not conform with the approved programme, the Engineer (or ER provided the necessary powers have been delegated) shall be entitled to require the Contractor to produce a revised programme, showing modifications to the original programme, necessary to ensure completion within the contract completion time or extended period, provided an extension of time in accordance with Clause 44(2) has been granted. Under Clause 46, if it appears that the rate of progress is too slow to permit completion by the prescribed or extended time for completion, the Contractor shall be notified accordingly by the Engineer (or ER if powers are delegated) and thereupon the Contractor must take, at his own expense, such steps as are necessary and approved to expedite progress.

EXTENSION OF TIME

21. Although powers to grant extension of contract time remain with the Engineer, it is the ER who will have to make an initial study of the Contractor's application for extension of time and report all facts relating thereto to the Engineer, so that he will be in

a position to assess any extension due or alternatively advise the Contractor that there is no entitlement to an extension of time. This in one of the reasons why it is so important for the ER to keep continuous, clear and accurate records of all matters which effect the progress of the works. It is important that the ER should merely report relevant facts to the Engineer and not his opinions. It is very easy for an ER to become frustrated or hence, perhaps unwittingly, prejudiced against a Contractor who, in his opinion is not performing as well as he should. Contractors have their own problems and provided the Engineer has all the facts, he is in the best position to assess an award for extension of time, be it an interim award, an award at the due date for completion or the final determination of extension of time, all of which are provided for in Clause 44(2) (3) and (4).

PROGRESS REPORTS

22.   The ER will be responsible for producing a monthly progress report for submission to the Engineer. Often and in particular on overseas work, the ER will also be required to send a copy of the progress report directly to the Employer. In such a case the Engineer will send his Engineer's report to the Employer separately, otherwise the Engineer will receive the ER's report and incorporate it with his own report before forwarding it to the Employer.

23.   The ER's progress report should be issued not more than one or two days after the end of the period covered by the report. A progress report which is ancient history is next to useless, except as a record. The Engineer and Employer are entitled to up-to-date information in the ER's progress reports and it is therefore necessary for all information required for the report to be compiled as the work proceeds. The ER's monthly progress report should, therefore, comprise copies of the programme and progress charts, records of matters effecting progress and photographs, with a minimum of text.

SITE MEETINGS

24.   The efficiency of an ER is inversely proportional to the time he spends at formal meetings.   Having said this, it is a good idea for the ER and the Contractor's Agent to get together at regular times, say once a week, to discuss and in as few words as possible, to record clearly matters requiring attention by one or the other. Each meeting should start with a review of the action taken on the points raised at the previous meeting.

25.   Large site meetings with Section Engineers, Quantity Surveyors and others and their opposite numbers on the Contractor's staff present are not to be recommended; the bigger a meeting the more valuable mantime is wasted. All supervisory personnel should have constant contact with their opposite numbers and the ER should be appraised of any matters which his staff feel should be taken up by him with the Contractor's Agent.

SITE INSPECTIONS

26.   The ER, together with the Contractor's Agent, should inspect the work on site on a regular basis, daily if possible. Discussions actually on the job often have much more value than at weekly meetings or by way of correspondence.   The ER and Contractor are on site to get the job done, not to sit isolated in their offices, only meeting occasionally, writing lengthy letters to one another and generally getting more and more bogged down in paper. It is necessary, of course, under the contract and otherwise, to put certain matters in writing but an ER should always, before writing a formal latter, say to himself, "Should I write a letter or can I deal with this verbally?"   Every letter from the ER is likely to breed several from the Contractor, who often has more staff to write them and is therefore in a strong position to play the ER at his own game and effectively tie him more and more to his office.   It is not undignified for an ER to walk over to the Contractor's Agent's office for a chat about the job. Some ER's misguidedly think it is.

SITE DIARY

27.   The maintenance of a comprehensive site diary in an ER's organisation is most important.   The ER must lay down clear instructions as to what should be recorded daily by each category of staff.   It is a good idea to have specially printed daily diary sheets which can be completed in triplicate.   Copies of Site Engineers' or Inspectors' diary sheets must be passed to the responsible Section Engineer daily.   Each Section Engineer must study these sheets and add his comments, in spaces provided for this purpose, before passing copies back to the originators for action on the comments as necessary and filing. Each Section Engineer will, in turn, produce his diary sheet, which will contain his overall daily report on the work in his section of the contract.   His daily sheet, in duplicate, backed up by the copies of his Site Engineers' and Inspectors' diary sheets, will be passed to the ER.   Daily diary sheets should be on the ER's desk by noon on the following day so that he can see them, note Section Engineers' comments, add his own comments and return copies to the respective Section Engineers the same day.   All diary sheets must be carefuly filed and securely stored in the ER's office.   The ER should, in addition, maintain his own confidential daily diary.   The ER's diary, together with the files of daily sheets will form the site diary.   The build-up of the diary as suggested, with all levels of supervisory staff contributing and with their contributions being scrutinised and commented upon daily, is a good method of spreading this daily chore, keeping everybody on their toes and ensuring a comprehensive record of the job.   The complete site diary must be passed to the Engineer when the ER's site office closes and will be held by him, for reference, until all matters connected with the contract or disputes arising therefrom, have been settled.

WORKS PHOTOGRAPHS

28.   Almost without exception construction contracts provide for photographs of the works to be taken when and where directed by the ER. Except in the case of remote overseas sites, the Contractor will employ a professional photographer who will visit the site, once a

month, in order to record progress at that time. In addition, part of the ER's equipment on site should be a good camera, available for use at all times, to record photographically anything which may be useful for future reference.

HANDING OVER SITE

29.   When the Contractor is not given possession of the whole site at the commencement of the contract but portions of the site are handed over at different times, it is essential for the ER to maintain a master plan on which is clearly indicated the portions of the site and the dates when they are handed over. It saves writing letters if a similar master plan is held by the Contractor's Agent and the ER and the Agent confirm hand over or take over on each copy of the plan. When necessary, it is useful also for the ER to agree with the Contractor a schedule of conditions at the time of handing over the site. Possession of the site is covered by Clause 42.

DETAILS OF SITE

30.   Before any work is commenced, levels of the existing ground should be taken and plotted on plans and cross sections which must be mutually agreed, signed and dated, by both the Contractor and the ER. One set of such drawings will be held by the ER and one set by the Contractor's Agent and again no time need be wasted in writing letters to one another.

31.   There is usually a specification clause covering the agreement of levels before commencement of work but whether or not this is the case, the ER's first action after the site, or a part thereof, has been handed over to the Contractor, should be to give notice to the Contractor's Agent, under Clause 56(3), of his intention to make measurements and take levels of the ground, before it is disturbed.

SETTING OUT

32.   The setting-out of all parts of the works must be checked by the ER. Such a check however, in no way relieves the Contractor of this repsonsibility for the true and proper setting-out of the works or for the correctness of the position, levels, dimensions and alignment of all parts of the works. This matter is fully covered by Clause 17 and it is normal, by way of a specification clause, to lay down the minimum notice, required from the Contractor, of his intention to set out lines and give levels for any part of the works so that the ER can make suitable arrangements for checking.

33.   It should be noted that, according to Clause 17, whilst the Contractor remains responsible for the correctness of setting-out, he is not liable for the cost of rectifying any error which is based on incorrect data supplied in writing by the Engineer or ER. The importance of check and double check on basic setting-out data, before such is supplied to the Contractor, cannot be too strongly stressed.

34.   A word here on base lines and bench marks: these have often been established before the Contractor and the ER comes to the site; at other times levels have to be brought in from some distance away and a base line has to be laid down before any setting-out can commence. Even though bench marks and base lines may

have been established on site and shown on the contract drawings, the ER should not take anything for granted but must, at the earliest opportunity, carry out all possible checks to establish, to his own satisfaction, that survey points and bench marks have not been disturbed and that the information given to the Contractor on contract drawings, in the specification or elsewhere is correct. All important survey points and benchmarks must be protected from damage or disturbance during the course of the works. A prudent ER and Contractor's Agent will arrange to offset survey points, at safe distances, so that the originals can be checked and re-established, if disturbed. Alternative bench marks should also be established in protected positions for use as necessary.

MATERIALS AND WORKMANSHIP

35.   The responsibility for ensuring that work is in accordance with the drawings and specification lies with the Contractor. The ER's function should, therefore, be one of quality assurance, to see that the Contractor's supervision and checks are operating. The ER must have a clearly laid down policy for supervision and inspection, which he should agree with the Engineer. This policy should stipulate such matters as what is to be inspected, frequency of inspection and the persons responsible for the inspections.

36.   Use of the right materials and good quality of workmanship are essential to the proper completion of any project. The ER has an important role to play in ensuring that these are in accordance with the drawings and specification. The origin and source of supply of materials should be checked and agreed, samples obtained and tested as necessary, manufacturer's test certificates obtained and studied and the Contractor's storage and handling arrangements on site agreed.

37.   With regard to workmanship, tests such as compaction tests on filling, cube tests on concrete and checking film thickness of protective coatings must constantly be carried out and recorded. Good workmanship depends not only on the materials used but also upon the quality of tradesmen, suitability of tools and plant, arrangements for carrying out the works including formwork, stagings and protective screens and coverings, proper control during operations and adequate care and protection thereafter. The ICE Conditions of Contract, together with a good specification, will provide the ER with all the necessary authority to ensure the provision of proper materials and workmanship.

VARIATION ORDERS

38.   Normally a delegation of powers by the Engineer allows the ER to order variations up to a limited amount, under Clause 51. Above such amount, the power to order variations is retained by the Engineer. It is important that variation orders, whether issued by the Engineer or the ER, are consecutively numbered and recorded, since they become part of the contract and in them the method of payment for the varied work is laid down and the item in the bills of quantities to which it is chargeable, is stated.

DAYWORKS

39.   Work to be carried out by dayworks should be specifically defined on each variation order or if the decision to carry out the varied work or any part of it is made after the issue of a variation order, an appropriate addendum to the variation order should be issued. The relevant variation order number, date and description and location of the work should be stated clearly by the Contractor on all daily records of labour, materials and plant and on all monthly priced dayworks statements which are required in accordance with Clause 52(3). It is very important that a proper system of recording all dayworks is set up, the daily records are checked and certified daily and the priced statements are submitted, checked and certified by the ER monthly.

MEASUREMENT

40.   An important area of the ER's duties is the measurement of the work. Final measurement and preparation of the final account should start on Day 1. Time should never be wasted on interim measurements, it should always be spent on final measurements. With few exceptions, final quantities of work can be determined from the contract drawings or supplementary contract drawings.   These quantities may have to be adjusted to take account of any subsequent changes but the availability of an accurate measurment, based on the actual drawings to which the Contractor has to work, will make the checking of interim valuations for monthly payment certificates simple, quick and easy. It is appreciated, of course, that some work, by its very nature, such as the toe levels of piles, exact excavation levels for foundations and volumes of rock in excavations, can only be measured when the work is done but as soon as the work is done, the measurement should be agreed between the ER and Contractor's Agent.

41.   Sheets should be prepared, in advance of pile driving, on which information from the pile driving records can be entered in such a form as to record measurements consistant with the relevant items in the bills of quantities. When pile driving, or a section thereof has been completed, the measurement sheets should be signed as agreed by both the ER and Contractor's Agent and the figures included in the final measurement.

42.   When a revised drawing is issued a record must be made of the state of the work at that time, to facilitate proper measurement and payment for the work actually done.

43.   Under Clause 56(3), reasonable notice has to be given to the Contractor, so that he may send a representative to participate in the taking of measurements. If he fails to do this, then the measurements made by the Engineer, or by the ER and approved by the Engineer, shall be taken to be the measurement of the work.

44.   Measurements must be properly recorded, either on dimension paper or in dimension books or in some other form which can be preserved and from which the various parts of the work can be identified. When recording measurements, the date on which they are taken, the names of the persons taking them, the part of the work being measured and the relevant drawing or drawings must be stated.

Measurements agreed with the Contractor should so state and be signed by both parties. Should the Contractor fail to be present when measurements are taken, copies of the dimension sheets should be sent by the ER to the Contractor's Agent, for his agreement.

CLAIMS

45.   Unfortunately, by their very nature, in most construction contracts circumstances arise in which the Contractor considers he is entitled to claim extra payment or higher rates for his work. Grounds for such claims could be adverse physical conditions and artificial obstructions (covered specifically in Clause 12), the interpretation of the specification, inconsistencies in drawings, inadequacy of the bills of quantities, condemned work or any other matters which the Contractor may consider should not be to his account or for which he feels he is not being fully reimbursed.

46.   When notification of intention to claim is received from the Contractor, in accordance with Clause 52(4)(b), he is also required, under that clause, to keep such contemporary records as may reasonably be necessary to support any claim he may subsequently make. Under sub-clause (c) of the above clause, the Contractor can be required to keep such contemporary records or further records as may be reasonable and material; therefore, when notice of a claim is given, the ER should ascertain what records are being kept and instruct the Contractor to make available these and any further records, for agreement. The ER may agree facts only and must not admit any liability.

47.   An important matter for an ER to note is, that whilst Clause 12 requires the Contractor to give notice of intention to make a claim persuant to Clause 52(4), it also clearly lays down the action to be taken, as soon as possible, by the Contractor and the Engineer, so that problems arising from unforeseen physical conditions and artificial obstructions may be dealt with expeditiously, thus minimising delay and cost effect.

MONTHLY PAYMENT CERTIFICATES

48.   It is important that monthly payment certificates should be delivered promptly for payment by the Employer. Often powers under clause 60(1) and (2) are delegated to the ER; he should never forget, in exercising these powers, that the Contractor is entitled to payment of the full money due to him, as soon as possible within the terms of the contract.

49.   The checking of the Contractor's monthly statement should be carried out quickly, based largely on recorded progress rather than direct measurement. The quantities of materials on site should be ascertained from records of materials received and used, checked as necessary by physical site assessment. The latter is particularly important, in the later stages of a contract, so as to ensure that materials not required for completion of the works are not paid for as materials on site. Dayworks records should be kept up-to-date and accounted for monthly. Should there be variation of price clauses in the contract then assessment of payment due to the Contractor, under these clauses, should be agreed and certified monthly wherever possible.

50.   When exercising his options under Clause 60(2) as to the amount to be certified, the ER must be satisfied that his actions are fair and not motivated by any desire to penalize the Contractor, possibly in the hope of encouraging him to improve his performance. However, if any work has been condemned or is in an unacceptable state, the ER is bound to refuse to certify or to certify a reduced amount, as the case may be.

FINAL ACCOUNT
51.   As stated earlier, the drafting of the final account should be started by the ER at an early stage. In a well run ER's organisation the completion of the final measurement, including variation of price assessments and dayworks, should follow very shortly after the substantial completion of the works. Accepting that the ER has been provided with an adequate and balanced site staff, if he or any member of his staff has to spend a long period, either on site or in the Engineer's offices, after physical completion of the works, sorting out final measurement, then the ER has not done his job.

AS-MADE DRAWINGS
52.   A set of contract drawings should be marked up to show, accurately and completely, the work as actually constructed. The Engineer will normally instruct the ER to forward AS-MADE drawings to his office as soon as each section of the work has been completed, so that full advantage can be taken of any slack periods when staff time is available for amending negatives to AS-MADE, ready for issue to the Employer, with the least possible delay, on completion of the works.

CERTIFICATE OF COMPLETION
53.   As the end of the time for completion approaches or if the date for completion has passed, the ER will find himself under pressure from the Contractor to recommend to the Engineer that a certificate of completion should be issued in accordance with Clause 48. It often happens, that the amount of outstanding work which the Contractor has given an undertaking, with his notice under Clause 48, to complete during the maintenance period, is unacceptably large. The ER should, with the Contractor's Agent, carefully record each item of work outstanding and the ER should then identify all items, on the list, which must be completed before a certificate of completion can be issued. Provided the non-completion of the work does nothing to prevent the Employer occupying or using the works, for the purpose for which they were intended, then normally there should be no reason why the ER should not recommend the issue of a certificate of completion by the Engineer.

CERTIFICATE OF MAINTENANCE
54.   Although, according the Clause 2(1), the supervision of the maintenance of the works is the ER's responsibility, it is not usual for the ER to remain resident on site, or even to be available to visit the site, during the period of maintenance. It is therefore usual for the

Engineer to make separate arrangements for any maintenance inspections. However, should the ER be available, then it would be desirable for him to inspect the works, on behalf of the Engineer, upon the expiration of the period of maintenance, so as to confirm that all necessary completion and maintenance work, as defined in Clause 61(1), has been carried out prior to the issue, by the Engineer, of the certificate of maintenance, in accordance with Clause 61(2).

9 The role of the Contractor

P. FITZPATRICK, BSc (Eng), DIC, FICE, FIHT, Chairman, Fitzpatrick & Son
(Contractors) Ltd

SYNOPSIS.   The Supervision of Construction by a Contractor is
a subject which does not lend itself to scholarly examination
as an engineering science; this Paper therefore is simply a
personal and subjective essay on construction as it should be
and unhappily as it so often is, and some of the factors which
have contributed to the difference.

1.   The use of the word "role" in the title conjures up a
casting procedure as in a film or play whereby the contractors'
agent and site personnel are selected to play their parts,
not as opponents, but as members of the same group of players
as the Engineer and his representatives. No fine distinction
is drawn between the Contractor and his agent nor between the
Engineer and his site representative(normally the Resident
Engineer). Each is, for the purpose of this discussion,
considered to be inseparable in the scenario. They must act
and react with the other harmoniously and constructively if
they are to create and maintain an atmosphere of co-operation
and teamwork on site in which good work is done quickly and
economically.
2.   Thus the first indispensible ingredient of a successfully
supervised contract is that the site agent and the Resident
Engineer should by psychologically compatible; ideally they
should both be likeable and agreeable people with the necessary
technical competence and experience. And each should have the
same script!
3.   To strengthen and reinforce the relationship a modest
allowance should be made in the contract budget of both sides
for entertaining the other to lunch once a week. Why the
Contractor's agent is allowed to charge a working lunch to
his company when the Resident Engineer is not has always been
a mystery. It is an unfair and divisive system that contributes
to the lack of prestige and dignity of the Engineer of which
more later.
4.   Of course the mental chemistry whereby a site agent and
Resident Engineer work positively together or fight from day
one is often beyond our understanding or control and for this
there is a simple remedy. There should be incorporated, if

not in the contract at least in the protocol of the industry, an agreement that in the event of contract disputes, bickering or other signs of discord, the Contractor and the Engineer will change both agent and Resident Engineer if either party requests it; and the site representatives should be made clearly aware of such an agreement.

5. Having cast the site agent and the Resident Engineer it is now appropriate to look at the supporting players. Both clerk of works and general foreman can have a significant influence on a contract. They are both of course in theory subordinate to the Resident Engineer and the site agent and therefore can be replaced in the manner previously described if disharmony persists. But it is questionable if some Contractors' agents have this authority and almost certain that a Resident Engineer has not. And yet how can a man be responsible for the outcome of a contract if he has no say in the choice of, nor power to remove, any of his staff. The Boston Tea Party was a protest against taxation without representation. Responsibility without authority is equally immoral and unworkable.

6. Hopefully therefore we now have the cast and all the players are vested with sufficient authority to perform their roles. Let us then set out precisely what the Role of the Contractor should be. This is not elaborated to provide a target for scorn. However idyllic it is in an imperfect world it is a goal; albeit one that frequently eludes us and of recent years has been receding farther into the realms of fantasy.

7. In an ideal world the Role of the Contractor, with no particular order of priority, is :-

(a) To establish and preserve a reputation for integrity, efficiency and quality of workmanship such that a client will happily invite him to negotiate or tender in limited competition for his work.

(b) To present an unqualified, unequivocal and straight-forward tender to execute the contract in accordance with the documents and if appropriate to submit a viable and measurably cheaper alternative for the consideration of the Engineer.

(c) When awarded the contract to execute the works in accordance with the drawings and to the quality demanded by the specification in an efficient and economical manner and within the contract timetable.

(d) To draw to the attention of the Engineer any potential weakness in the design and to put forward proposals for its correction.

(e) To use his knowledge of local materials and their characteristics to improve the overall quality and durability of the works and if appropriate offer cost savings where marginal but suitable materials are available.

(f) To use his ingenuity and experience to provide the

Engineer with practical, workable and economical solutions to the unforseen problems which always arise.

(g) To debate, confide, discuss and if necessary conspire to defeat the forces of nature and bureaucracy that ceaselessly toil for their mutual downfall.

(h) To complete the works within the contract time and for the contract sum, subject only to agreed variations, and submit a final account with no extracontractual or contractual claims.

(i) Then to bask in the adulation of a contented Engineer and a satisfied client for a job superbly executed to a high standard; and thereafter to enjoy the psychological and financial rewards of his labours.

8. In any kind of world where integrity and fair dealing have a value, the Role of the Contractor is not:-

(a) To submit a tender that is based primarily on the strategy of first obtaining the contract at almost any price.

(b) To await the often predictable changes created either by external forces or by the Contractor's own connivance and endeavour to exploit them to the client's disadvantage.

(c) To stand back complacently watching the embarrassment of the Engineer.

(d) To call for quantity surveyors and lawyers to produce a massive document impugning the Engineer's competence and claiming lack of detailed or timely information.

(e) To argue for a period of years whilst the facts become forgotten and the client becomes tired of the dispute and then

(f) reluctantly to settle for a fraction of the disputed amount which was in any case many times the justifiable or hoped for settlement.

Can anyone who recognises this second Role as standard practice wonder why the industry is searching for a new form of contract; surely a recognition that the industry has lost its way.
9. What then are the circumstances and the conditions responsible for these changed standards. Primarily it is the lost dignity and authority of the Engineer, stolen by a bureaucracy that grows and feeds on the continuous and insulting examination of his competence and integrity. All life is controlled by the whip and carrot; but such is the top heavy and destructive bureaucracy that sits above the Engineer no carrot is left. He is not empowered to reward, only to condemn, and the Contractor reacts in the only way available to him – to apply the letter and not the spirit or intent of the contract.
10. In 1977 the C.C.S.J.C. (Conditions of Contract Standing Joint Committee) in response to the disquiet in the industry prepared some Guidance Notes which were a thoughtful, simple and yet naive confirmation of the Engineer's role.
11. A joint statement just published by this Institution and the clumsily entitled Chartered Institution of Public Finance

and Accountancy has done little to help the situation. It has in fact in a well intentioned effort to clarify the position merely enshrined the basic heresy of questioned authority of the Engineer as accepted practice in our industry.

12. It is always easier to criticise a document than to produce or improve it: but in a classic example of damning with faint praise many seem to have accepted it on the basis that it was not such a total disaster as previous efforts.

13. An examination however of the starting point of their study, the Contract Audit Guidance Notes published by CIPFA will demonstrate the abysmally low basis upon which their recommendations were founded. It reads like a criminal charge sheet. Nothing other than the Engineers' personal habits and family life appear to be outside the scope of the inquisition.

14. Control over the Engineer is not overt but is exerted by inference and this is what makes it difficult to resist. The insidious nature of these formalised investigations by non-technical people is tantamount to a complete emasculation of the Engineers' powers. They would be justifiable in the event that the Director of Public Prosecutions had indicated that there was prima facie a case of conspiracy or fraud to answer; but these investigations are applied to Chartered Civil Engineers of unquestioned integrity as a matter of routine.

15. Can it be shown that they produce enough evidence of malpractice over the years to save sufficient of the tax-payers money to justify their large direct cost and the huge indirect disruptive cost? Of course not.

16. The fifth edition of the ICE Standard Conditions of Contract presupposed an unbiased Engineer beholden to neither client nor contractor. It also presupposed a contractor who has priced the work at rates which will show him a reasonable profit without contractual claims. Neither of these two suppositions pertains today. It is incredible that the first contractual event is the appointment of an Engineer by one party to the contract who is clearly empowered to dismiss him at will; but even this is not the nub of the problem.

17. He must constantly be haunted by the fear that the auditors might find any instance where he has demonstrated generous treatment to the Contractor and could thereby be accused if not overtly, then by inference of incompetence, or worse, collusion.

18. And this highly trained and noble individual is face to face with a Contractor's agent not just hungry for additional profit but desperate to avoid the ignominy and loss of employment which would follow a heavy loss or bankruptcy.

19. And where is the natural selection process whereby the Engineer has the power to discriminate between the good Contractors and the bad ones at the invitation stage. With a few notable exceptions the selection process is in the hands of accountants and administrators who have little knowledge of or interest in how a Contractor performs on site, or whether he is an incompetent rogue or a dedicated professional; that, they say, is the Engineer's problem.

20.   The sole criterion in the choice of a Contractor should be the Engineer's experience backed up by the provision of a performance bond. The bond market will, if properly used (and bank bonds eschewed), determine a Contractor's stability and financial competence to execute the work more efficiently than any other selection process.

21.   And a new and strange phenomenon has entered upon the construction scene which further illustrates the ignominious position of the Engineer. Any change in method, use of material or for that matter any engineering decision involves an element of risk no matter how small. The young and inexperienced Engineer is understandably frightened of the unknown and will not approve it; the mid career Engineer has to balance his entire future which might be at risk against no possible personal gain. It follows that the only Supervising Engineers who can demonstrate the essential ingedient of change (namely courage) are those nearing the end of their career who are largely immune from the long term effects of their decisions; they know that the only people protected from the claws of the clients' auditors are the trustees of their pension fund!

22.   This is in no way intended as a criticism of the Supervising Engineers who are by and large every bit as good as the Contractors they work with. It merely reflects the appalling consequences of a system whereby the Engineer is subject to a higher, usually faceless and often technically ignorant Authority.

23.   In many ways the Engineer under the contract assumes the mantle of a judge. He has to be and be seen to be wise, perceptive, considerate, incorruptible and impartial. He is required to hear all the facts, albeit in a laborious and tedious but painstaking fashion; then to deliberate and then to make his judgement. His judgement is only questioned by recourse to a higher court and probably a tribunal of other judges. But can you imagine a system whereby the judge's office is in the hands of one of the litigants; or His Lordship's judgement could be overturned by a committee, quantity surveyor or district auditor?

24.   And if the parallel of the judiciary is not to your taste, consider a contract as a game of football. One team (the Contractor) pits his wits and muscle against his opponents (the forces of nature) and the Engineer is referee. Let no one be surprised at the disarray when the only authority given to the referee is to send a man off the field; the right to reward by the award of a free kick or penalty having been abrogated to the owners of the football ground who also reserve the right to question the referee's every decision.

25.   These parallels may seem distant from the theme of the Contractors Role but they are at the root of his interpretation of the part he is allowed to play and the quality of his performance.

26.   The Role of the Contractor in those forms of contract fashionable today such as management contracts is not within

the scope of this paper, having been dealt with elsewhere.
27.   There is however an important group of problems created
by today's tendency for the main Contractor to employ little
or no direct labour and to sub-contract the entire scope of
the works assuming only a management role. He is of course,
unlike a pure management contract, exposed to an element of
risk; but he has, unlike his sub-contractors, some protection
under the contract. These specialist sub-contractors,
unaffected by union problems and usually run by their owners,
are frequently efficient, industrious and ambitious little
companies desperately trying to survive and expand in a tough
competitive world. Their management knows little and cares
less about the subtleties of contract phrases and expects
to be treated and paid fairly for a job well done; but they
are at the mercy of a main Contractor's agent, possibly
desperate to make an underpriced contract profitable.
28.   In the event of a dispute he has the ultimate sanction
irrespective of any form of sub-contract which may or (may not)
have been entered into. He just withholds or delays payment
until either the sub-contractor concedes and complies or
goes into liquidation.
29.   The form of sub-contract for use in conjunction with the
ICE Conditions of Contract is currently under review by the
Federation of Civil Engineering Contractors and the sub-
contractors associations (FASS and CASEC). The use of this
form is widespread and should in theory offer protection to
the sub-contractors. But used with a contract based on the
fifth edition it is often extensively modified by the main
Contractor by striking out those conditions that provide the
protection; and in the case of a package deal or lump sum
contract it is usually not offered at all. Thus the contract
on which so much time and energy has been spent in an effort
to provide justice for all is effectively giving protection
only to the privileged few. It is a matter of conjecture as
to the extent to which this situation contributes to the top
of the league position that construction perpetually and
unenviably holds in the bankruptcy lists.
30.   And a plea finally for a change which would have a real
effect on the Role of the Contractor in supervising contracts.
31.   The numbers of supervisory staff on contracts in this and
the last decade has grown out of all recognition. It is not
just the enormous expense of site accommodation and maintenance
that is incurred but the much greater cost of disruption. It
is in the nature of any supervisor to wish to justify his
existence by proving his utility and worth. Frequently
inexperienced though well read, they have no alternative but
to demonstrate their value and indispensibility to their
superiors by inflicting the letter of the specification upon
the Contractor; and let us be clear about one thing. It is
not difficult to work to the letter of the specification, it
is impossible.
32.   Many Contractors will tell you that they feel obliged to
match these destructive and unnecessary site supervisors man

for man in the hope of neutralising them.

33. At a recent meeting with an eminent American Engineer it was generally agreed that mile for mile of road or pound for pound of contract value, the British Contractors were subjected to three times the number of supervisory and control staff as their U.S. counterparts.

34. And let none of the foregoing dissuade an Engineer from finding (and paying well) some mature, time served tradesman who knows not just whether the materials comply but more importantly whether the site personnel placing or fixing them are skilled in their trade and capable of producing first class work. Often if they are not he can help or teach where weaknesses are apparent to him. No newly fledged first class honours graduate can do that.

35. Mark Twain was accused of saying that everybody talks about the weather but nobody does anything about it.   The Role of the Contractor is the one that has been thrust upon him but we can do something about it.

(a) Reinstate the Engineer as the supreme authority, answerable only to the courts.
(b) Halve the number of site supervisors but double their experience.
(c) Let the Engineer be the sole arbiter (with appropriate non bank performance bonds) as to who is invited to tender for a contract. And let his selection be influenced (as it will be) by who is a good Contractor and not by who is a good lawyer.

Does anyone doubt that this would help to reinstate the pleasure and satisfaction in what is essentially a creative and exciting business to work in and that the Contractor would then take up his true Role.

REFERENCES

1. Guidance Note 2A: Functions of the Engineer under the ICE Conditions of Contract. Issued by the ICE Conditions of Contract Standing Joint Committee. Reference CCSJC/GN2AB/September 1977.
2. Joint Statement for Engineers and Auditors issued by The Institution of Civil Engineers and the Chartered Institute of Public Finance and Accountancy.
3. Contract Audit Guidance Notes issued by the Chartered Institute of Public Finance and Accountancy (March 1983).
4. Form of Sub-Contract for use with the ICE General Conditions of Contract (The Federation of Civil Engineering Contractors).

10 The role of the Site Agent

S. J. I. SHIPP, MA (Cantab), MICE, Director of Mowlem (Building) Limited, London

SYNOPSIS. The term "Site Agent" described the leader of the contractor's team on site. The size and nature of the site team will be determined both by the demands of the particular project and by the contractor's policy on the location of support functions either on the site or at regional office. Whatever the size and scope of the site team, the site agent's personal performance as team leader will be the major factor influencing the quality and success of the job.

1. In order to define areas of responsibility for supervision it will be helpful to describe and name the components of the site team that might be found on a large multi-disciplinary job. It is envisaged that the site agent, or project manager, holds absolute responsibility for all the activities taking place on the site, and is responsible to a remote central office manager for all aspects of the job's performance. The site team will be subdivided into sections covering as many as five main disciplines. Each of these section leaders may be considered as being at equal level of responsibility within the site team even though the basic level of seniority may vary and the size of each section be quite disparate. Since different companies designate different areas of responsibilities to a given title, the title and brief job description of each of the section leaders is given.

Site Agent

| Construction Manager | Project Engineer | Planning Co-ordination | Services Manager | Quantity Surveyor |

2. The Construction Manager is responsible for all physical activity on the site. Under him come a team of foremen whose task it is to ensure that the site runs smoothly, that materials are moved as intended, and that the many problems that occur in a construction project are smoothly overcome. Within his team trades foremen are responsible for ensuring that standards of workmanship are achieved. The demands on the construction manager are continuous and taxing. He must

not only be capable and experienced, he must also have stamina and durability, and a personality powerful enough to impose his will upon the course of the job.

3.   The Project Engineer will lead the team responsible for all aspects of engineering, method development, and site control of the construction process. As well as establishing and maintaining dimensional control of the works, his team will perform a progress-chasing role on a number of activities.

4.   The Project Planner is responsible for all planning and co-ordination on the site. In addition to the production, monitoring and updating of all the requisite programmes, he will be responsible for the management of information flow between the design team and the specialist sub-contractors. He will be responsible to the site agent for the production of regular progress reports required to monitor the progression of all aspects of the job from start to finish.

5.   On jobs with significant services content a building services manager will frequently lead the site team in all aspects of this work. His responsibilities will include co-ordination of services information flow between the design team and services contractors, co-ordination of the services builder's work requirements, vetting sub-contractors' installation programmes, evolving consolidated programmes for plant areas, and managing and monitoring the installation.

6.   The Project Quantity Surveyor is responsible for the financial, contractual and commercial aspects of the job. He leads a team responsible for purchasing and procurement, preparation and issue of sub-contract enquiries, appraisal of tenders, placing of sub-contracts, measurement of the work and application for payment. It will be his task to keep the site agent continually abreast of the commercial performance of the job. The site agent should derive considerable support from this team of section leaders, and by the exercise of his leadership he should build a team whose joint capability exceeds the sum of its parts.

7.   The broad objectives which the site team seek to fulfill are to construct the job in accordance with the parameters already set in respect of quality, time and cost. It is unlikely that any of these objectives will be met unless the site is run efficiently. One of the pre-requirements for the smooth running of the site is the set-up, and the responsibility of devising this naturally devolves upon the site agent with his team. Starting off with the plan of action and programme derived at the time of tender it is the site team's job to make a more detailed analysis of all aspects of the job, the site and its surroundings. Taking account of all phases of construction they must make detailed plans that provide for access for delivery of materials, un-loading and storage areas, materials handling plant, and set aside areas for accommodation and welfare of operatives to-gether with office accommodation for supervisory and

management personnel. In checking the feasibility of their preferred solutions to matters of access and adjoining properties they will need to consult with police, local and statutory authorities. If the site is in an urban area it is unlikely that these enquiries will have been made at the time of tender. The decisions made on the nature of the site set up are of fundamental importance to the subsequent efficiency of the site, particularly where there is little or no free space. In reaching these decisions the site agent will be guided by information from his team, but will also rely largely upon his own experience and instinct. At this starting point his role is akin to that of a stage manager setting the scene for the action to follow.

8.   The achievement of the desired quality of work is always one of the site team's primary objectives, and its importance is universally accepted. What is sometime forgotten is that a team input is required to the planning and method development to create the conditions on the site where good outputs of work of the desired quality may be achieved. The site agent will ensure that the working conditions planned for each operation and trade have been checked to allow for ease of access, delivery of materials, and ready access to setting out points for dimensional checks. Whilst it is not impossible for accurate and unblemished work to emerge from an untidy site, reliable work can only be achieved by systematic and tidy working procedures. The standards of achievement of accuracy and tidy, systematic work practices are set very early in the job. The site agent, through his construction manager and project engineer, will be the judge of the standard to be accepted. In doing so he will have set his personal stamp upon the job.

9.   In order to maintain control of programme achievement and of quality control it is essential that the site agent has rapid access to records of each work area. These records are often in the form of daily diary sheets, and should record such items as the number of operatives working in a particular area, the physical progress made, materials delivered and used, delays encountered, and any technical items of note. The diary sheets should be completed at the end of each day and filed in the site office. Monitoring of progress against site programmes will normally be carried out at least fortnightly. The site agent will scrutinise any areas of unsatisfactory performance, and an analysis of the daily record sheets may assist in shedding light on the underlying causes. It will be necessary to ensure that corrective action is taken as rapidly as possible to remedy any areas of deficient progress. If significant lateness is allowed to build up it will almost certainly ruin all efforts made to achieve a satisfactory finalcial result to the job. Hence the experienced site agent will not only adopt a ruthless attitude over any lack of performance that may arise, but will also take scrupulous care that progress in all areas is systematically monitored.

10.   In making arrangements for the physical set-up on site, the site agent will be guided principally by his construction manager. The main decisions to be taken will be influenced by practical matters, and experience should be the main ingredient. The most fundamental decision to be taken is the choice of vehicle access for materials delivery. In City centre sites there may be few options available. Once this decision has been made, it will be necessary to arrange for servicing of the unloading area by materials handling plant - coverage by tower crane and access to material hoists where necessary. It is common practice in urban sites with basement construction for significant temporary works to be required, and to move the access point during the phasing of construction. In the course of deliberations on these matters consultation with the police and local authorities will be required. In contrast, on sites where there is an abundance of potential storage area, judgement will be required to determine the economic solution to amount required and the method of utilisation.

11.   The provision of accommodation and welfare facilities for the site labour force is another area in which the construction manager will provide guidance to the site agent. It is common practice for the main contractor to provide these facilities for all sub-contractors in addition to his own men, and thus a reasonably accurate forecast of the numbers expected is required early on. There are cases in urban sites with footpath-to-footpath development where considerable ingenuity is required to find sufficient space for drying rooms, toilet facilities and the canteen. In cases of this nature it is common to resort to a combination of cabins perched on gantries outside the building line together with temporary use made of areas within the building where minimal finishes are to be applied. It will, however, be necessary to arrange connection of temporary water, drainage and power supplies for these facilities, and a once-only set-up for accommodation at ground level, clear of the building, is to be greatly preferred. The canteen should be capable of providing a simple range of hot snacks for the mid-day meal break. If it is well run it will discourage the tendency towards the "wet break" and thus make a contribution to safety and good timekeeping.

12.   The site agent will attach the greatest importance to maintaining high safety standards on site. Not only is this right in principle, but poor safety provisions can lead to industrial relations problems and reduced outputs. He may choose to designate his construction manager as holding a special responsibility for carrying out his safety policy, and will insist that all staff undergo regular safety training. He will insist that safety is designed into the working methods from the start, and that particular care is taken with high risk areas such as means of access to external works. The construction manager will ensure that adequate arrange-ments are made for first aid treatment on site, and that

instructions for dealing with serious injuries are clearly understood. The inspection and re-stocking of the first aid supplies will need to be carried out on a regular basis.

13. The construction manager will normally take responsibility for arranging temporary supplies of electricity for all plant and temporary lighting, temporary water supply and connection to foul drainage for the welfare facilities. In making these arrangements he may be assisted by building service manager.

14. During the early stages the site agent will depend upon the project engineer and his team for the method development for all the engineering work. The basic construction plan from the tender period will be taken as the starting point in formulating the construction strategy. A detailed study of the Engineer's and Architect's drawings is required at this stage, combined with careful study of the specifications. Particular attention must be paid to the tolerances permitted in the design, and these should be checked against the characteristic tolerances required by specialist building finishes. Conflict between specified tolerances can sometimes be found when granite cladding is specified to a concrete face, and the void between the back of the granite panels and the face of the concrete may become too narrow to accommodate granite fixing brackets. From this study of the drawings, the specification and tolerances, methods of construction appropriate to the task will be developed. The project engineer's team will be responsible for all aspects of this development work, from the design of temporary works to uphold excavations during the groundworks to agreeing day joints in the concrete pours to the roof with the Resident Engineer.

15. The site agent will also look to the project engineer to provide within his team all the necessary expertise on survey and setting out of the work. The importance of this work is fundamental. Of the various setbacks that a job may suffer, there is nothing more demoralising than building something in the wrong place. The site agent will insist that this work is done in a systematic manner which incorporates a mandatory checking procedure. It is adviseable to have all fundamental survey work checked by a separate method, and also to ensure that on secondary work, such as marking out offsets from gridlines, that the work is checked by a different individual prior to concreting. The experienced site agent will recognise the crucial importance of accurate setting out, and will ensure that priority is given to obtaining good access for this work to be done.

16. Another of the project engineer's team's responsibilities will be the provision of quality control. This will entail the keeping of a detailed set of records of a large number of inspections and tests. Where concrete is being used he will become involved in obtaining approval of mix designs, preliminary test results, and supervision of the concrete from the batching of the aggregates to the placing

and surface treatment. He will arrange for all the site tests of concrete and the series of test cubes that will be required. A similar involvement will also be required if structural steel is the construction material, although more off-site inspection and testing will be required in this case. An increasing involvement by engineering staff is now required in the supervision of granite cladding. Recent doubts in some circles as to the traditional approach to the fixing process have demanded a more rigorous site testing of fixings, and detailed record keeping.

17.   In addition to responsibilities in method development, dimensional and quality control, the project engineer's team will also perform a progress-chasing and monitoring role throughout the primary construction process. Depending upon the size of the job, the engineering team is frequently divided into sections with a section engineer taking responsibility for all aspects of engineering construction in that area. In reinforced concrete construction this will lead to considerable attention being paid to the reinforcement. This will entail study of the drawings and schedules, programming and calling forward deliveries of reinforcement from the supplier, supervision of the fixing by the operatives, and checking the work prior to concreting. In sorting out the inevitable clashes and errors on the drawings and schedules with the Resident Engineer it is almost essential that the site team engineers have had detailing experience in a drawing office. The inspection of a complicated area of reinforcement by the section engineer and Resident Engineer prior to concreting is an area in which differences of opinion can arise over interpretation of the drawings and specification. The project engineer will keep a close watch on progress at this stage to ensure that differences of opinion are viewed in a pragmatic manner, and that a positive attitude is adopted in resolving differences. The site agent will be aware of the importance of the time element and will authorise the measures necessary to maintain progress.

18.   The site agent will attach considerable importance to the relationship which develops between his site team and the Client's inspectorate. This relationship will be at its most productive when genuine respect is held by each party for the professional capability and role to be played by the other, and for the individuals concerned. It will be best to recognise that there are both positive and negative elements contained in the role of the inspectorate, and to determine to build early on the positive aspects, so that relationships can get off to a good start. It is often sensible to agree the acceptance standards of workmanship for the trades at an early stage, and this may take the form of samples being carried out on the site, or visits to earlier jobs. At this stage the site agent must adopt a policy of total realism in indicating the range of standards that he intends to produce. The roles of the contractor's team and the inspectorate are

largely complementary, and the site agent will ensure that a spirit of harmonious team working is built up and maintained. Once this team spirit has been achieved, disagreements and discussions on points of detail may be resolved in a businesslike and professional manner.

19.   In the preceding paragraphs an attempt has been made to define the role of the site agent and the scope of the supervisory duties of his team. The emphasis placed upon the duties of the team has been intentional. It is generally accepted throughout the construction industry that jobs are built through team work and not by a series of individual "star roles". Hence the role of the site agent, the leader of the contractor's team, is an absolutely crucial one. He must inspire the individual section leaders of his team to give a first rate performance, and by his leadership weld all the components into an effective operating unit. He must also include in his team in a very real sense the sub-contractors and their labour force. Having achieved this important goal, he must then recognise the role to be played by the other teams employed by the Client, such as the design team, and ensure that his team operate efficiently and harmoniously with them in a positive and constructive manner. When he has achieved all of these objectives he is on the path leading towards a successful job.

Discussion on Papers 7–10

MR E. JAMES, Senior Lecturer, Hatfield Polytechnic

I would like to support what Mr Deuce has said about having black and white with no grey. We are in a world of compromise where standards are falling. As professional engineers we must not let this happen in the construction industry. Take for example consulting overseas. I know of a local firm in the Far East who have an excellent reputation for being unbribable.

This has spin-off as clients can trust them: this must be good for business!

MR P. J. INGRAM, Civil Engineer, Sir Robert McAlpine & Sons Ltd, London

Over twelve years' experience as a contractor I have found that on civil engineering contracts the Engineer generally does perform his duties to the standard outlined by Mr Deuce.

Unfortunately, perhaps because of the fragmentation of the professional term in the building industry, this is not always so in the supervision of building contracts. Mr Deuce: do you think that engineers should take over all responsibility for building contracts?

MR T. L. G. DEUCE

I am heartened to hear of your experience. It can be no secret that architects have abdicated much of their responsibility to quantity surveyors and clerks of works who loom large in the supervision of building contracts. This happens to a much lesser extent in engineering contracts and, as I have said in my paper, could amount to fraud when it does. I know of several large building contracts which have engineers as supervising officers and I believe they are being supervised to the highest of professional standards. Thus I agree that engineers are perfectly capable of such work. However, I see no particular reason why this should become

more widespread. What is essential is that the architects
entrusted with the work carry out their duties as supervising
officers with true professional diligence. If they are not
prepared to do so they should say so in order that a proper
and acceptable alternative supervising officer can be
appointed.

DR N. M. L. BARNES, Martin Barnes & Partners, Stockport

In this discussion we are patting each other on the back by
attributing total impartiality under the contract to the
Engineer. The reality is that the Engineer is analogous to a
referee in a football match with only one team on the field –
the Contractor's team which is trying to score – to increase
the contract sum and to secure extensions of time. In the
absence of a team pushing the other way, the referee must push
against the Contractor to stay in the middle. With a very
attacking contractor's team, the Engineer himself may have to
attack. Is this compatible with total impartiality?

MR I. D. LIVESEY, ICI plc, Blackpool

Further to the comments on responsibility for health and
safety on site I would like to add that if the construction is
carried out on property already occupied by the employer then
he also has legal responsibilites for the safety as the
'occupier'.
  Mr Deuce: would you comment on who the Engineer to the
contract should be in the situation where the Employer has a
strong in-house engineering design function but has engaged a
consultant to design and supervise a project? Both the
client's engineering director and the consultant's partner are
suitable candidates with advantages and disadvantages.

MR T. L. G. DEUCE

I doubt whether there can be any hard and fast rule in such
circumstances. In many instances my Authority employs
consultants to design works but supervises the construction
with its own staff. In these circumstances I or another
suitable member of the in-house team act as the Engineer. In
other situations, when short of site staff, we have employed
consultants' staff to be resident on site to supervise work
designed in house but I have nevertheless been the Engineer.
  There is a tendency in some management contracts to appoint
a member of the Managing Contractor's staff to be the Engineer
or the supervising officer but to retain one or two salient
functions such as extensions of time or settlement of claims
in house. This can work quite well if it is felt that there
is a need to retain some vestige of control in house, provided

128

of course that the arrangements are clearly spelt out in the contract documents. In general I take the view that if a consultant is to be entrusted with the design and construction then one of the consultant's staff or partners should be appointed as Engineer. I do not subscribe to the practice of naming 'the Partnership' as the Engineer.

MR J. C. FERGUSSON, London Transport Executive, London

The appointment of a Management Contractor as the Engineer appears to be a revolutionary suggestion. How and why has this been done, and how has the arrangement worked in practice? Can a Management Contractor in this role be as impartial as an employer's own Engineer? Is the client the Employer in contracts netween the client (Employer) and the construction contractor(s)?

Mr Deuce: could you elaborate on ex gratia payments and offer a few examples of where this has been recommended?

On one of our contracts, under 5% of the provisional sums, contingency items and daywork bill contained in the tender were expended. As these formed 25% of the tender sum, the Contractor feels that he is entitled to some loss of profit and overheads. There seems to be no claim under the contract, but morally he may have been misled over the amount of work he would probably have to carry out.

MR T. L. G. DEUCE

Management Contractors have been employed for a variety of reasons. Sometimes this is done to facilitate so-called fast track working; sometimes on complex projects to aid the supervision of a multiplicity of contractors or sub-contractors; sometimes to bring the expertise of a contractor to bear during both the design and construction phases and yet again simply because the Employer may have engaged several engineers and architects to design the works but has inadequate or insufficient in-house staff to supervise the construction and is reluctant for various reasons to choose between the designers.

The client would certainly be the Employer in the contract with the Management Contractor and often would be the Employer in those sub-contracts which the Management Contractor lets on the client's behalf but this does not necessarily have to be the case. It all depends on how the Employer wishes the contract to be written.

I am not prepared to quote examples of specific contracts where ex gratia payments have been made. The types of circumstances where they might be thought to be applicable are those where the Contractor has suffered a loss due, for instance, to changes in tax imposed by the government during the currency of a contract. Other similar changes caused by force majeure and over which the Contractor had no control and which are not provided for in the contract could provide acceptable grounds. The point which must not be lost sight of is that ex gratia payments are by definition only made voluntarily and then only when it is judged right to do so in the particular circumstances by good employers.

I am reluctant to comment on the example quoted as I do not know all the circumstances but I would have thought a contractor misguided to have included some of his inevitable overhead costs in uncertain items and I should need a lot of convincing that he had in fact done so. If firm items had been removed then that would be quite a different story on both counts.

MR G. M. HANNAH, Partner, Hannah, Reed & Associates, Cambridge

Mr Deuce: what is your view on the responsibility of the Engineer in connection with the checking and approval of workshop drawings and fabrication details. I assume that having carefully checked and approved such drawings the Engineer does not relieve the Contractor of the responsibility for erecting the structure in accordance with the contract – in the same way that the Resident Engineer's check of the setting-out does not absolve the Contractor of any errors which may have been overlooked.

MR T. L. G. DEUCE

The Engineer clearly has a moral responsibility with respect to approvals he has given but I believe that the provisions of clause 14(7) would apply if the ICE form is used and that the Contractor would not be relieved of any of his responsibility by reason of the Engineer's consent.

MR R. FREER, Engineer, Pencol Engineering Consultants, London

Mr Deuce: you have spoken of the different methods of building design and control that you use and I should be grateful if you could tell us what factors you consider in selecting the type of control to be used.

Is management contracting better for a particular type of building, or when particular time scales and financial objectives are to be met, and in what circumstances would the employment of a consultant or lead consultants be the preferred option?

MR T. L. G. DEUCE

Without going into great detail I find it difficult to enlarge

significantly on the answer given to the first part of Mr
Fergusson's question. However, there is unlikely to be a
viable case for the employment of a management contractor on
an uncomplicated project. The more complicated or involved a
contract becomes the more likelihood there is that a
management type of contract would be justified. The
multiplicity of trades involved in modern buildings with their
increasing dependence on air-conditioning and electronic
control systems etc. make them increasingly likely to benefit
from this form of contract. Speed is certainly another factor
as are major changes introduced at the last minute and the
need or desirability of involving a contractor in the design
process while maintaining a full range of options for
subsequent competitive tendering.

The employment of a consultant is certainly the preferred
option wherever only one consultant had been responsible for
the design of the project provided that he was experienced in
that type of construction. Indeed in the general case I would
probably favour the employment of a consultant whenever I felt
that the complexity of a project was within his compass.

MR J. DALLAWAY, Supervision Manager, Ove Arup Partnership,
London

Mr. Sweetapple: could you clarify your approach on quality
assurance and quality control, and what comments do you have
on this function being discharged, in the main, by the
Contractor?

What is the approximate cost as a percentage of the contract
sum of the site supervision that you envisage?

Finally, the Health and Safety at Work Act says in effect
that everyone is responsible for everyone else, and that the
Engineer on site has to do something if he thinks dangerous
conditions exist, otherwise he may be prosecuted.

MR E. JAMES, Senior Lecturer, Hatfield Polytechnic

In paragraph 4, Mr Sweetapple, you state that 'only the
Contractor is responsible for the safety of all operations on
site'. Please will you clarify this further as it does not
seem to tie in with the Health and Safety at Work Act.

MR J. R. SWEETAPPLE

My approach to quality assurance is as stated under the
heading MATERIALS AND WORKMANSHIP in paragraphs 35, 36 and 37
of the paper. Quality control should be in the hands of the
Contractor and quality assurance should lie with the
Engineer's Respresentative. Here quality assurance means (a)
making sure, as far as possible, that the Contractor's and his

131

suppliers' quality control is adequate and satisfactory and
(b) the carrying out of or arranging for independent checks as
a routine when considered necessary or in particular cases of
doubt. Having in mind the different usage of the words
quality assurance there is no conflict between the section on
MATERIALS AND WORKMANSHIP in Paper 8 and the section headed
QUALITY ASSURANCE, paragraphs 40, 41 and 42, in Paper 11.

The cost of site supervision varies according to the type,
size and complexity of work, what is to be included in the
consultant's fee for the site supervision, what services are
to be provided under the Contract and what services are to be
provided by the employer. The location of the site is also a
factor which can increase the cost of supervision and while it
may be argued that the cost of site supervision, as a
percentage, would not be greatly affected since the contract
sum is likely to be higher for remote sites, this is not
always the case, particularly when local contractors are
appointed. In view of all the variables it is not really
possible to state meaningful percentages.

The object of paragraph 4 of Paper 8 is to emphasize the
necessity for an Engineer's Representative to be on his guard
against the all too common temptation to tell the Contractor
how to run his job, thereby relieving the Contractor of his
responsibilities under the ICE conditions of contract.

There is no conflict between what is said in the paper and
the Health and Safety at Work Act and in this respect
attention is drawn to the final sentence in paragraph 6.

It is important that, in the supervision brief provided by
the Engineer to the Engineer's Representative, the provisions
of the Health and Safety at Work Act 1974 (particularly
Section 7) are emphasized. The supervision brief should make
it incumbent on the Engineer's Representative to instruct his
staff of their responsibilities and actions regarding safety
on the site. All matters affecting health and safety on site
should be reported to the Engineer's Representative who must
be instructed that, in case of doubt about the action taken or
further action required, he is to report the facts immediately
to the Engineer.

MR P. FITZPATRICK, Chairman, Fitzpatrick & Son, Hoddesdon

Chairman, Ladies and Gentlemen
I must commence with an apology particularly following the
scholarly addresses of Mr Deuce and Mr Sweetapple. What
started as a simple essay describing the role of the
Contractor degenerated uncontrollably into a rabble-rousing
harangue against the establishment.

But just as the City of London has gained a reputation
abroad for great drinkers and lunchers, so English contractors
have established a name for being great lawyers, and just as
the appalling food at large Spanish hotels has spawned a whole
industry of small restaurants, so contractors and the

emasculated engineers who confront them have created a whole industry of claims, consultants, surveyors and lawyers.

I am not trying to put Mr Abrahamson out of business – I may need his help one day – but as a doctor is called to a sick patient he is needed on a sick contract (by definition almost certainly one with an inadequate or impotent (for whatever reason) Engineer. This should be a rare and unusual occurrence not on every other contract or (as in the case of major motorways) eight out of ten.

Could we possibly learn from other trades and disciplines? Let me quote two clauses in policies available to underwriting members of Lloyds – I am sure there are many other examples in different fields.

(a)   LLOYDS CONTINGENCY ESTATE PROTECTION

This Agreement shall be construed as an honourable undertaking between the parties hereto not to be defeated by technical legal construction, it being the intention of this Agreement that all further liabilities emanating from the Reinsured's participation as an Underwriting Member of Lloyd's are removed in the event of death and are assumed by Reinsurers hereunder.

(b)   LLOYDS STOP LOSS POLICY

The Arbitrators and the Umpire shall interpret this insurance as an honourable engagement and they shall make their award with a view to effecting the general purpose of this insurance in a reasonable manner, rather than in accordance with a literal interpretation of the language, the true intention of the parties being that the Insurers shall follow the fortunes of the insured.

Could we not look at the spirit and not the letter of the contract?

There are I am sure many in this assembly who, whilst welcoming this approach, have reason to be cynical about its application. At the same time there are others in this hall who can vouch for the fact that it can be made to work.

In 137 contracts varying between £50000 and £4 million over 12 years we have had only two formal claims and these were both requested by the Engineer as the only way that he could reimburse us for circumstances outside his, or our, control.

The role of the Contractor is not made easier by this approach and it is a painful furrow to plough alone; fighting by Marquis of Queensbury rules when the competition is using its boots can never be easy.

I do not for one moment doubt that by skilful manipulation of the contract document some losing contracts could have been saved and others made more profitable, but if we do not claim to eat as well as the competition I can assure you that we sleep better, and so do the Engineers that we work for.

MR T. L. G. DEUCE, Deputy Engineering Director, British
Airports Authority

The increasing use of sub-contractors increases Dutch
auctioning. Is this why there is less and less activity by
the main contractors and increasing dependence on sub-
contractors? How can Dutch auctioning be stopped?

MR P. FITZPATRICK

The increasing use of sub-contractors is largely created by
tax, employment legislation and fears of union activity.
   The respectable specialist sub-contractors who are a vital
part of the industry have suffered grievously at the hands of
main contractors who amend the sub-contract form of contract
and pay slowly. Dutch auctioning after a contract award is
the norm in the industry and is apparently accepted. Yes, it
is serious and undesirable but I have no solution.

MR W. H. EDEN, Engineering Manager, Southern Water Authority,
Brighton

I have worked for Mr Griffiths' 'water quangos' for ten years
and during that time have been subjected to the attention of
auditors and to the other difficulties of organizational life.
Whilst I sympathize with your sentiments about the 'creeping
emasculation' of the Engineer, Mr Fitzpatrick, do you think
that we are in danger of becoming over protective of our
position in relation to contracts? It is, I suppose, natural
human behaviour to want to be regarded as omnipotent and
infallible, but is it a wise policy? Why should we not be
criticized by auditors and other non-technical representatives
of the organizations for which we work? Why should we not
expect to answer such criticisms and to justify our actions?
After all, if the Employer is not satisfied, he will dispense
with our services and this is true whether the Engineer is an
employee or a consulting engineer.

MR P. FITZPATRICK

I think this is a question of emphasis. Certainly the
Engineer should not be above the law and is always in the last
resort subject to the courts, but the routine checks
recommended by CIPFA contain almost a presumption of guilt.
They must inhibit his freedom to make decisions and certainly
affect his impartiality.

MR J. R. SWEETAPPLE, Rendel, Palmer & Tritton, London

Mr Fitzpatrick's paper could not have been written better by
the Engineer! Regarding his wish that the number of site
supervisors should be halved, referring particularly to
overseas projects, some years ago it may have been the case
that projects were over staffed with supervisors. This is a
bad thing in itself: site supervisors should have a full day's
work and they become a nuisance if they merely have to justify
an existence. Nowadays this seldom occurs when generally
consultants have to bid for all the work they can obtain and
often a client stipulates what he is willing to pay for each
category of site supervisory staff. Clients also wish to
approve all site staff employed by the Engineer and whilst the
Engineer will insist on having adequate staff on site it is
seldom that he can persuade his client to authorize more staff
than nominated in the Consultant's bid.

MR P. J. INGRAM, Civil Engineer, Sir Robert McAlpine & Sons
Ltd, London

I have experience of a civil engineering contract where the
final account was subject to audit by the Employer. It was
one of the contracts for the Tyne and Wear public transport
executive for the construction of the Tyneside Metro.
   The Engineer fulfilled the role envisaged by the ICE
conditions and successfully resisted any attempt by the
auditors to interfere with his decisions. Nevertheless, the
Employer was kept well informed of decisions on site and their
financial implications. This ensured that the audit was a
formality and in the event the only effect of the check was to
correct an arithmetical error amounting to about £100.

MR P. FITZPATRICK

You were fortunate to have a powerful and respected firm of
consultants battling for you. Can you imagine what chance a
directly employed Engineer would have, or a little firm of
consultants, when even the mighty Mott, Hay and Anderson had
trouble?

MR D. J. LEE, G. Maunsell & Partners, London

The problems of interference with the Engineer by auditors and
other parties is not disputed but does not the same problem
arise when the directors and head office staff of a contractor
interfere with the authority of the site agent?

MR P. FITZPATRICK

Yes it does indeed; that is why remote contract sites (i.e. remote from the Contractor's head office) are often the most efficiently run.

I was, many years ago, asked to take over a failing joint venture contract as Project Manager. The conditions I made were (1) that I would have arbitrary and unfettered authority in all matters and (2) that none of the consortia directors would visit the site without my express permission which would invariably be withheld. To my surprise this was formally accepted.

The contract recovered strongly and would probably have never had its problems had the prior incumbent been granted these powers.

MR E. JAMES, Senior Lecturer, Hatfield Polytechnic

Mr Fitzpatrick: will a high volume of claims continue to flow from contractors if and when the current depression in the construction industry ceases, i.e. when the volume of work increases will you be able to operate on larger profit margins and use your 'claims engineers' on production instead?

MR R. A. WEBB, Senior Project Designer, Dorman Long Bridge & Engineering Ltd, Bedford

Working for a steelwork contractor I would not necessarily agree with Mr Fitzpatrick's statement about halving the number of site supervisors, but I agree about doubling the amount of experience.

In paragraph 33 he states that the Americans have three times less supervision than we have in this country. I do not know what the position is with highways but almost every time I pick up Engineering News Record I read of a bridge falling down, welds cracking or bridges failing after 10–12 years' service and so perhaps there is a good reason for the level of supervision in this country.

MR P. FITZPATRICK

The trouble here is that if a bridge fails it is news and makes the headlines, if it stands up for ever it is forgotten. Road failures number 50 to every bridge collapse but they are not usually sensational enough to merit attention. It has always been a mystery to me why bridges are designed to a factor of safety of 4 and roads to 0.9.

MR R. FREER, Engineer, Pencol Engineering Consultants, London

In paragraph 7 Mr Fitzpatrick says that he would like
'limited' competition or a 'negotiated' tender.

It is obviously a waste of everyone's time for the client
to send tender documents to 14 potential tenderers when four
would be adequate, but would you not be aggrieved if you were
excluded from a tender list for a job for which you thought
your company was eminently suitable and capable of
undertaking.

Consulting engineers make the Contractor's life too
difficult by issuing documents which are too long to read
thoroughly, particularly since the method of measurement. used
is probably different from that which the Contractor uses
himself. Would you consider that it would be better for the
tenderer to submit the tender in the form he prepares it and
for the client to assess and negotiate from that point.

My understanding of the word 'claims' as we have been using
it this morning is the difference between the tenderer's price
and the price he realizes that the job will cost when he has
had time to digest the documents and drawings and all the
implications of the work thoroughly, and which he hopes he
will recover from perhaps loose wording in the contract
documents. Do you consider that the form of tender I have
suggested, coupled possibly with payment to contractors for
genuine tenders, would avoid this problem of claims?

MR P. FITZPATRICK

We were recently excluded from a tender list for a contract
for which we had for many months expressed interest and had
investigated in depth. So the question is not hypothetical
and we were sorely aggrieved, but not because we were left off
but why we were left off. In spite of the Engineer's strong
recommendation the decision was made, effectively, by an
accountant based solely on the value of the contract and the
fact that there were contractors many times our size who had
applied for the papers. Professional and technical competence
apparently counted for little.

The second point concerning the concept of contractors
preparing their own contract is that a comparison becomes
difficult; any time we have attempted to prepare a contract
document we have come to realize how clever those much
criticized draughtsmen of the fifth edition of the Institution
contract really were.

Paying contractors for tenders could, much like some drugs,
create more problems than those it set out to cure, but
certainly the cost of tendering is substantial and clients
that invite long lists of contractors (like one London borough
that invited 23 contractors for one contract) should be
charged.

MR D. J. LEE, Partner, G. Maunsell & Partners, London

Much of the earlier discussion on the role of the Engineer and
the Resident Engineer has highlighted the erosion of their
designated power in the last 20 years or more. Mr Shipp: your
interesting paper concentrates on the agent but it would be
interesting to hear your comments on the impact of other
members of the Contractor's team such as the contract managers
and directors. It must be many consultants' experience that
the agents' powers and characteristics can pale into the
background when the Contractor takes a view of handling a
contract technically or financially somewhat differently from
that which the Engineer or his representative would seek.
   The client has his fleas and little fleas, so does the
Engineer. What about the Contractor?

MR J. DALLAWAY, Supervision Manager, Ove Arup Partnership,
London

The Project Engineer's role appears to have conflicting
requirements:

   Progress-related activities may assume priority over
      quality control checks which are not essential to
      progress. How well were these conflicts resolved on
      the National Westminster Bank?
   How big was the Project Engineer's team?
   How big was the Resident Engineer's staff?
   How was quality control split between them?

MR D. C. TWEEDALE, Group Engineer, Hertfordshire County
Council

Do accountants within a Contractor's organization put
pressures on the site agent which distract him from getting on
with supervising the job as well as he could if left alone -
and have they in part led to the increase in claims?

MR P. HIGGINS, R. Travers Morgan & Partners, East Grinstead

I should like to ask Mr Shipp and Mr Fitzpatrick two
questions. Firstly, the authority of the Resident Engineer is
required by the contract. Would it not be helpful to have the
Agent's authority also delimited? As an example of the need
for this, I cite the requirement for a completion certificate
under the ICE conditions. This must be accompanied by an
undertaking by the Contractor. Can this be properly given by
the Agent?
   Secondly, on a separate topic, do you agree that
contractors have lessened their involvement in material
quality control and now rely principally on the Employer's

materials testing consultant for control of material?
  If so, do you feel that this is the correct attitude for
Contractors to take?

MR P. FITZPATRICK

It would be perfectly reasonable for the employing authority
to be advised of the Agent's powers. Indeed it would probably
help the Agent as much as the Engineer if a board resolution
outlining his authority was required by the contract.
  The large sums in major contracts set aside for the
establishment of site laboratories and their equipment tend to
persuade contractors that enough testing is enough and that
further duplication is not required. The smaller contractors
without materials testing staff are inclined, as they do with
setting out, to leave testing to the Resident Engineer's
staff.

MR J. T. GRANT, Brian Colquhoun & Partners, London

Presumably the ARIBA (JCT) form of contract was modified to
allow for the presence of the Engineer. Would you comment on
the effectiveness of this arrangement, Mr Shipp?

MR D. FINEBERG, Rendel Palmer & Tritton, London

Do Mr Fitzpatrick and Mr Shipp feel that engineers had
adequate training/experience to become effective agents?
  Was undergraduate/postgraduate education sufficient to
ensure adequate knowledge of
leadership/administrative/industrial relations aspects of the
job?

MR P. FITZPATRICK

We certainly do not receive appropriate training. John Mott
of French Kier once wrote a penetrating article in one of the
professional journals stating that the majority of university
examination questions gave satisfaction to nobody other than
the academics. Only now are the courses becoming more
relevant although generally anything connected with business
studies is deliberately ignored in undergraduate courses.

MR P. J. CEARNS, Soils & Materials Engineer, Suffolk County
Council

Is it not probable that the number of site staff is a symptom
of the weight of correspondence which appears to develop

between the Agent and the Resident Engineer?

MR P. FITZPATRICK

Certainly the lack of personal contact between the Engineer's
Representative and the Contractor's Agent breeds letter
writing which in its turn breeds contention and contentious
letters. These all need careful attention and additional
staff.

11 The implications of testing

P. J. CEARNS, MICE, MIMunE, FGS, Soils and Materials Engineer, Suffolk County Council

SYNOPSIS. The importance of specifying parameters which can be effectively checked, and of stipulating acceptable tests is discussed. The problems of test reliability and frequency are mentioned, as are methods of assessing test results for reliability. Non-destructive tests have some part to play in assessing quality, and their use is briefly discussed. In conclusion, the use of alternative payment schemes and quality assurance schemes are advocated.

THE TESTING REGIME

1. The necessity for testing materials and workmanship is beyond doubt. Methods and levels of testing, and the criteria for the interpretation of results are not so universally accepted, and the implementation of corrective measures in the event of non-compliance is often the cause of considerable dispute.

2. To obtain the optimum benefit from the considerable effort which can be put into testing, the testing regime should be determined at the project stage and allowed for in the specification.

3. The specified testing regime should allow for:
   - i) the relationship between design stresses, loading frequency and design life.
   - ii) the desired durability, and aesthetic uniformity.
   - iii) the existence or type of quality assurance schemes.
   - iv) the limitations of the test methods.
   - v) the standard of testing staff available.
   - vi) the standard of laboratory, and facilities available for checking test reproducibility.
   - vii) the compliance system to be used in the contract.

STANDARD OF TESTING

4. Unreliable testing is of no value whatsoever, but all tests have their limitations. The confidence limits of the test method must therefore be appreciated in order to specify parameters and evaluate results.

5.   In evaluating results, the tests themselves should be subject to reliability checks. The commonly used criteria for test evaluation are:-

    i)   repeatability, (r) - Quantitative expression of the random error associated with a single test operator in a given laboratory obtaining successive results with the same apparatus under constant operating conditions on identical test material. It is defined as that difference between two such single results as would be exceeded in the long term in only one case in twenty in the normal and correct operation of the test method.

    ii) reproducibility, (R) - Quantitative expression of the random error associated with test operators working in different laboratories, each obtaining single results on identical test material when applying the same method. It is defined as that difference between two such single and independent results as would be exceeded in the long term in only one case in twenty in the normal and correct operation of the test method.

    iii) confidence limits - The tolerances on a parameter within which the true value will lie for a given probability.

        Example - A satisfactory check on a concrete compression test machine might show a mean strength of 73.4 N/mm^2, a standard deviation of 1.76 N/mm^2, and a difference with the reference machine, which had a standard deviation of 1.16 N/mm^2, of -0.2 N/mm^2. The confidence limits would be shown as "-2.8% to +2.4% for 95% probability", i.e. there is only a 1 in 20 chance of the true difference of the results from the machines laying outside this range.

6.   The typical standards to be attained for four of the more commonly employed tests are shown in Table 1. However, even these limits can only be reliably met if proper care is taken in adherence to the specified procedures in laboratory management, the training of staff, and the design and maintenance of apparatus. Laboratories should be subject to external checks wherever possible. The Cement and Concrete Association's facility for checking concrete cube compression testing is well known, and other schemes exist for the checking of bituminous materials testing, laboratory weighing, etc.

7.   A more comprehensive and rigorous laboratory accreditation scheme has recently been introduced under the National Testing Laboratory Accreditation Scheme (NATLAS) for the complete evaluation and accreditation of laboratories for a variety of tests. It should, however, be noted that the possession of a NATLAS accreditation certificate only certifies the laboratory

Table 1. Examples of Testing Reliability Limits

Test	Standard	Repeatability	Reproducibility
Concrete Cube Compressive Strength	BS.1881 Part 116 1983	Repeated for pair - 10% of mean	-
Grading of Aggregates for Bituminous Materials	BS.598	5 to 14% depending on sieve size	7 to 18% depending on sieve size
Binder Content of Bituminous Material	BS.598	0.3%	Base and Base-course and Coated Macadams
		0.2%	H.R.A. Wearing Course
P.S.V. of Roadstone	BS.812	6.0	4.9

for the tests specified, and not necessarily for all the tests the laboratory carries out.

8. If a formal certification is not possible, quality checks on the laboratory should still be made, including:-

  i) checking experience and ability of staff.
  ii) careful checking of apparatus design and serviceability.
  iii) regular checking of results on samples against known values and/or other laboratories.

9. The selection of laboratory equipment for site use must be rational to be effective. Often, unnecessarily elaborate equipment is provided in site laboratories where simpler, more reliable, and better calibrated equipment would be of more use. Whenever possible it is better that the Client or Engineer provides site laboratory equipment for the Contractor, in order that the appropriate quality of apparatus can be on site at the particularly critical first stage of construction.

SELECTION OF SPECIFIED PARAMETERS

10. The designer's or specifier's quandary is frequently whether to state his quality requirements either directly or indirectly. Frequently, it is not possible to apply a direct requirement, e.g. the true, or even accelerated durability of paint, or the permeability of asphalt, would be difficult to measure reliably, and would require many years of testing. Thus, indirect tests are frequently needed.

11. Indirect testing can be extremely effective if there is

both good theoretical basis for its use, and good correlation with the desired feature, provided that the limitations of the test are understood. For instance, the weather durability of rolled asphalt in relation to recipe specification is well established, although the rutting durability is not reflected by the recipe specification. To minimise rutting, it is normal practice to use other indirect measurements such as Marshall stability, flow, etc.

12. Generally, in specifying tests it is better to consider only tests which are of established reliability. Only where no other option is available should a non-standard test be used, and then only if the apparatus and method are carefully defined. Measurements of soil or aggregate permeability, for example, can vary by an order of magnitude depending upon the method used to compact the sample (without consideration of apparatus design and other variables).

TEST FREQUENCY AND EVALUATION OF RESULTS

13. To allow quality to be properly evaluated, it is imperative to have statistically meaningful results. This would be easily attainable if all things were uniform. Unfortunately, perfect uniformity is not possible. Variabilities exist in:-

      i) the works (materials variability),
      ii) sampling,
      iii) testing.

14. Usually, the Engineer is confronted only with test results, reflecting the combined effect of the three variabilities. Frequently, an approximation of the sampling and testing variability can be estimated either from field trials or published work. But, more usually, the accept/reject decision can only be made with confidence on the evidence of a sequence of results. It is therefore necessary to judge quality without being influenced too much by the occasional rogue result. Condemning localised sections of the works on the basis of single rogue results is obviously futile, if for no other reason than other (unsampled) parts of the works may have equally poor sections and yet be allowed to remain in place. Clearly, it is necessary to have a regime of testing which will truly reflect the whole quality of the works. To establish such a regime, it is necessary to determine the test frequency.

15. Where the nature of work control, and location, are consistent, the required frequency of testing may be established by experience. Appendix 1 gives examples of the frequency of testing applicable to roadworks under normal conditions in the U.K.

16. If no previous production records are available, test frequency must initially be high, perhaps testing each load of reinforcement steel, batch of concrete, or mix of asphalt. Once a run of, say, 20 or so results is available, the information may be displayed, and the important aspects noted, viz:-

(a)   variability of result.
(b)   relationship between project results and
      laboratory trial results.
(c)   the relationship of the mean, and variability
      to, the specified value.
(d)   the scatter of results relative to the
      observed level of production control.

17.   If the initial testing shows the works to be both
satisfactory and consistent, then the sampling rate may
reasonably be reduced. If not, remedial action will need to
be taken, including possibly a close examination of sampling
and testing methods.

18.   Once test results are submitted, they must be considered.
All too often, if the results meet the specified limits, they
subsequently are cast to one side and the supervisor turns his
attention to other more pressing matters. When a "failure" is
reported, hours of valuable supervision time, and often construction time, are wasted whilst the results are validated
and remedial action determined.

19.   Validation of a test result is an exceedingly complex
procedure, even for relatively simple products which have a
restricted number of specified parameters. If time and progress are to be saved, the validity of testing should be kept
under constant review.

20.   Warren (ref. 1) has described the assessment of data
from the concrete cube test, and his procedure exemplifies the
difficulties of test validation thus:-

      Firstly, the factors affecting the measured
      strength must be appreciated, viz:-
        i)   sampling and re-mixing,
       ii)   normal variabilities,
      iii)   cube making,
       iv)   curing,
        v)   testing,
       vi)   recording.
      The normal variability comprises two primary
      components, viz:-
      V_w = within batch variability.

      V_t = testing variability.

      The influence of these variabilities may be
      reduced by increasing the number of increments
      taken per sample (Ns), and/or the number of cubes
      made per test (Nc).
      V_w will vary from 4% to 12% (from good to
           acceptable)
      V_t will vary from 2% to 4% (for good testing)
      Ns is normally 4 (B.S. 1881).
      Nc varies according to the specified standard
         from 1 to 3.

$$\text{if } x = 1.96 \sqrt{\frac{V_w{}^2}{Ns} + \frac{V_t{}^2}{Nc}}$$

then the "true mean strength" will be between

$$(\frac{100}{100 + x}) \quad \text{and} \quad (\frac{100}{100 - x})$$

If a result is proved to be invalid, the tracing of the source (or more usually sources) of error can be very time-consuming. The causes of possible errors include:-

i) incorrect sampling.

ii) sampling or sub-sampling being systematic instead of random.

iii) cube moulds - bad assembly, maintenance or manufacture.

iv) poor cube making, site storing, stripping or transport.

v) poor curing.

vi) testing - platen flatness,
platen alignment,
platen location,
cube location,
rate of loading, particularly close to failure.

vii) recording - booking in,
recording load,
density,
misinterpretation of load chart etc.

Not all the possible testing errors can be evaluated after the test. Hence it is most important to consider test cube data routinely before failures occur, in order to prevent:-

i) unsuitable material being accepted.

ii) sound material being rejected.

With proper plotting and consideration of results, and then observing:-

i) unusual variability.

ii) variability between cubes of the same set - normal pairs should not vary by more than 12.5% of the mean, and the test result would certainly be invalid at 18.5% of the mean (for sets of 3 cubes, the equivalent figures would be 15% and 20% respectively).

iii) unusual density variability.

iv) correlation between 7 and 28 day strengths.

Once any anomalies are detected, their cause should be thoroughly investigated before erroneous accept/reject decisions are made.

21. The philosophy applied by Warren applies to all engineering materials testing, although for many, the problems of validating test results is more complex. When the number of parameters involved in, say, bituminous analysis is considered,

the problem of validation becomes almost impossible to treat for most projects, other than intuitively.

22. For such materials, any validation of results is normally carried out from experience, unless an unusually large project is being constructed, such as a major international airport.

23. Statistical methods of evaluating results for all materials have, for many years, been advocated by materials engineers, but have won only limited acceptance by the majority of the civil engineering profession. C.P.110 (Ref 2) has, however, gone some way to introducing the "acceptable risk" concept by the introduction of the "characteristic" strength definition.

24. In 1969, Hardman (ref. 3) of the Transport and Road Research Laboratory (T.R.R.L.) introduced a continuous assessment system for rolled asphalt, which relied on the premise of a "producer's risk" (of having acceptable material rejected) of 5%, and a "consumer's risk" (of accepting non-acceptable material) of 50%. The system treated each specified recipe parameter separately and required the continuous evaluation of "the last 20" test results by an elegant system of control charts, from which the accept/reject decision could be made. Fig. 1 shows a typical chart.

25. The system was applicable to either large projects or a series of smaller projects supplied from a common plant or plants. It was capable of incorporation into contracts, with or without a fixed penalty system.

26. Warren, Hardman and others have produced schemes for rationally considering the trend of results on a statistical basis, in order to avoid the possibility of the Engineer or Contractor being alarmed or consoled by individual results. Very few workers have taken the procedure a step further in order that the full implication of the accept/reject decision might be formalised.

ACCEPTABILITY WORKS

27. Methodical compliance schemes have the dual effect of improving quality and defining exactly the degree of non-compliance when it is present. However, seldom do they define what action is to be taken when test results indicate the non-acceptibility of quality.

28. All too frequently, when the tests indicate non-compliance, the further consideration is applied only to the area thought to be represented by poor results. In fact, substandard results, either in absolute values or variability, are more likely to indicate general or random inadequacy, rather than specific failure.

29. Investigation into "failed" areas is often carried out by non-destructive testing. Such tests have their applications, although their use in these circumstances may not always be appropriate. The main problem in the application of non-destructive testing data is due to the fact that most estimate the required engineering parameters indirectly, and require

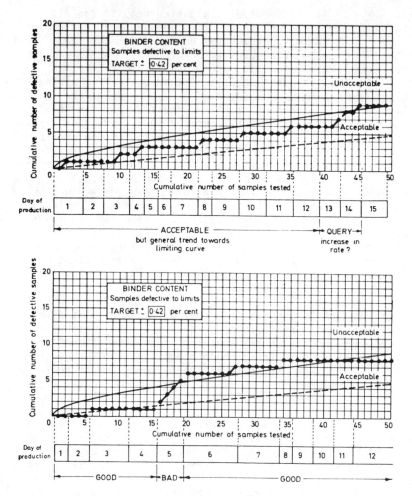

EXAMPLES OF CONTROL CHARTS FOR NUMBER OF SAMPLES DEFECTIVE TO "10 PER CENT" LIMITS OF COMPOSITION FOR ROLLED ASPHALT

FIG.1.

(After Hardman, 1969)

"on-the-job" empirical calibration or back up research and development calibrations. The non-destructive measurement will normally be influenced by more than one property of the work being examined. The use of a second non-destructive system measuring other properties or preferably "overlapping" properties, can be most instructive in assessing results. For example, ultra-sonic test results are strongly influenced by the dynamic modulus value (which in turn is usually related to ultimate and yield strengths) but are also inversely related to density. However, gamma radiation transmission is primarily related to density. Hence, by performing two sets of tests it is possible to obtain a much better estimate of a strength parameter than by a single test.

30.   The claims made for many non-destructive methods often vastly exaggerate their usefulness; also the data always requires expert interpretation, as it can often give optimistic results if, say, the influence of carbonation in concrete on the rebound value is ignored.

31.   Non-destructive tests are of greatest use in comparing the properties of materials against known standards; even in these circumstances care must be taken to ensure that the test environments are compatible, e.g. the rebound value or pulse velocity will not be the same in an extracted free-standing laboratory specimen as it was when the same material was constrained and stressed insitu.

32.   The interpretation of non-destructive tests is beyond the scope of this paper, but has been reviewed by Bungey (ref. 4), and many of the tests are detailed in B.S. 4408 (ref. 5) and A.S.T.M. D2922 (ref. 6).

33.   Having obtained non-destructive test data and successfully correlated it to the specified parameters, it is then necessary to consider whether the works are of the desired, or even adequate, quality. It is assumed that the investigation included all work that could be affected by poor quality control, not only that work in the area represented by the original samples.

34.   In arriving at a decision as to whether to accept the so called "failed" material, all the required properties must be considered. The designer may, for instance, have specified a high characteristic strength in a concrete in order to feel assured that he would, on average, obtain also a better durability*. Thus, even though the strength may be adequate relative to design stresses, the life of the structure will be reduced if the density, cement content, etc., are inadequate. Making decisions based on other than specified parameters may thus be seen to be complex.

35. How much better it would be to use only the specified parameters. Indeed, this is possible if the testing is carried out properly, at the correct frequency and with the consequences

* It is not always the case that good durability is synonymous with high strength, but this is not important to the present argument.

Table 2. Table of Penalties* (after Van de Fliert and Schram - ref. 7)

Penalties per 2000 m² - guilders

Layer Thickness	Roadbase: 0.15 m. Sand Cement or 0.12 m. Sand Asphalt	Basecourses of 0.06 m. Bitumen-bound Gravel (per course)	Basecourse or Wearing Course of 0.04 m. Asphaltic Concrete
Shortfall on Thickness			
1-5 mm.	-	-	-
6-10 mm.	-	-	2000
11-15 mm.	-	2000	4000
16-20 mm.	1000	4000	6000
21-25 mm.	2000	6000	8000
etc.	etc.	etc.	etc.

Compressive Strength: Sand Cement	
Strength too low**	Penalty per 2000 m² in guilders
0.1-0.5 MN/m²	1000
0.6-1.0 MN/m²	2000
1.1-1.5 MN/m²	3000
1.6-2.0 MN/m²	4000
2.1-2.5 MN/m²	5000
etc.	etc.

Bitumen Content: Asphaltic Concrete	
Bitumen Content too low	Penalty per 2000 m² in guilders
0.1-0.2%	-
0.3-0.4%	1000
0.5-0.6%	2000
0.7-0.8%	3000
0.8-0.9%	4000
etc.	etc.

Voids: Asphaltic Concrete	
Voids too high	Penalty per 2000 m² in guilders
1%	-
2%	1000
3%	2000
4%	3000
5%	4000
etc.	etc.

* The amounts quoted in this table were applicable for the years 1974-1977. At the beginning of 1978 most of the penalties were increased by 50%.

** Strength shortfall with reference to the criterion of at least 2.0 MN/m² applicable for the period 1972-1977. At the beginning of 1978 this requirement was reduced to 1.5 MN/m².

of non-compliance established before the errant test results
are submitted.

36.   In the Netherlands, the Public Works Department (State
Road Laboratory) exercised a system of financial penalty, based
on test results from 1969-1978. The analyses were made on cores
drilled from the completed pavement. Thus, considerable onus
was put on the contractor to control the quality of his work
during construction. Van de Fliert and Schram (ref. 7) have
reported the system, and Table 2 illustrates the application
of the system.

37.   As a result of working the system over 300 projects, the
State Road Laboratory was able to develop a new statistical
system which makes allowance for the consequential shorter service life resulting from sub-standard work.

38.   Suffolk County Council Highways Department introduced a
compliance system for rolled asphalt in 1971, which required a
higher sampling rate than described by Van de Fliert and Schram,
but from which checks on quality could be made during the progress of the works. Unlike the Hardman system, it assessed all
the principle attributes of each sample simultaneously, and
also stipulated the consequence of non-compliance. It did not
have the same statistical reliability as the Hardman system.
None-the-less, it has been found to provide a useful criterion
for the assessment of rolled asphalt.

39.   The principles of the scheme may be summarised thus:-

1.   Rate of Sampling

Daily delivery of each type of Load	Rate of Sampling
100 tonnes	1 per 20 tonnes
100-200 tonnes	5 per day
200 tonnes	1 per 40 tonnes

2.   Rating of Material for Compliance

(a) 1 penalty point to be applied for each:-
Complete 1% error in stone content beyond B.S.
tolerance.

Complete 0.1% error in binder content beyond
B.S. tolerance.

Complete 0.2% error in filler content beyond
B.S. tolerance.

Complete 10% error in grading on each specified
sieve beyond B.S. tolerance.

(b) the penalty points for each sample to be
summated.

(c) the total penalty points for each successive
5 samples are summated and tabulated, i.e.
the totals for samples 1-5, 2-6, 3-7, etc.
are recorded.

3. <u>Action to be taken for non-compliance:-</u>

(a) where number of penalty points in last
5 samples <5 - accept material.

(b) where number of penalty points in last
5 samples, 6-15, reduce payment for
material covered by the 5 samples by 10%
per penalty points in excess of 5.

(c) where number of penalty points in last
5 samples >15 - remove and replace all
material covered by last 5 samples,
except that for courses other than
wearing courses, sections of material may
be allowed to remain if the Engineer is
able to satisfy himself that the material
to remain is confidently assessed as
closer than 25% of the tolerance range to
the specified target value.

QUALITY ASSURANCE

40.   In many fields of engineering, the responsibility for
setting control limits and determination of quality levels
lies firmly with the supplier. This practice can be extended
to civil engineering through contract provisions.

41.   The words "quality assurance" are often used rather
more loosely than is desirable. However, for the purposes of
this paper the phrase "quality assurance" is taken as referring
to a system whereby the supplier or contractor establishes an
integrated system of production, systematic monitoring of his
raw materials and components, and quality management. The
supplier then takes full responsibility for the ultimate
quality of his work, including the quality, experience, and
qualifications of personnel employed in production and testing.
Such systems can only be of any real benefit if they are then
open to free inspection (either by the Engineer or a truly
independent authority) which should, at least initially,
include a series of random test checks.

42.   Having set up a satisfactory quality assurance scheme,
the need for direct testing by the Engineer is removed. Also,
the evaluation of results becomes a matter of "control" rather
than "compliance". Although quality assurance is already
functioning in the cement industry, and is likely to become
rapidly established for other bulk manufactured materials, it
is also likely to be some years before it becomes fully
established in the civil engineering supply industries, steel
fabrication, ready mixed concrete, bituminous materials, etc.

ACKNOWLEDGEMENT

The author wishes to thank Mr. G. Stansfield, County
Surveyor, Suffolk County Council, for permission to publish
this paper, and the staff of the County Laboratory for their
help in its preparation.

REFERENCES

1. WARREN P.A.   Assessing the validity of the cube test result.   Cement and Concrete Association, TDH 8449, London, 1976.

2. C.P. 110 (1972).   The structural use of concrete.   British Standards Institution, London.

3. HARDMAN R.   L.R. 276,   A system for the judgement of compliance with specifications for rolled asphalt to B.S. 594. Transport and Road Research Laboratory, 1969.

4. BUNGEY J.H.   The testing of concrete in structures. Surrey University Press, London, 1982.

5. B.S. 4408.   Recommendations for non-destructive methods of test for concrete.   British Standards Institution, London, 1974.

6. D.2922.   Standard test methods for density of soil and soil aggregate in place by nuclear methods (shallow depth). American Society for Testing and Materials, 1981.

7. Van de FLIERT C. and SCHRAM H.   Ten years of quality control in road construction in the Netherlands. Rijkswaterstaat Communications Government Publishing Office. The Hague, 1979.

Appendix 1. Example of Typical Testing Rates for Sample Items of Roadworks

Process or Material	Purpose or Type of Test	Relevant Clause in D.Tp. Specification	Relevant Standard	Minimum Rate of Testing	Maximum Rate of Testing
Backfill/ Filter Material	Grading	505	Table 5/1	1 per source	1 per 200 tonnes
	ACV	505	BS.812	1 per source	1 per 100 tonnes
	Sulphate Content	505	BS.1377 Test No.10	–	
	Plastic Limit	505	BS.1377	1 per source for Type A	1 per 100 tonnes
	Slag Stability and Sulphur Content	505	BS.1047	1 per source	1 per 100 tonnes
Granular Sub-base	Grading	803, 804	BS.1377 Test No.7	1 per 4000 sq.m.	1 per 1000 sq.m.
	Moisture Content	804	BS.1377	1 per 4000 sq.m.	1 per 1000 sq.m.
	CBR	804	BS.1377	Nil	–
	Plasticity Index	803, 804	BS.1377	1 per source	1 per load
	10% Fines Value	803, 804	BS.812	Nil	1 per source
	Optimum Density Curve	804	BS.1377	1 per source	–
	Frost Susceptibility	801	MM.64	Nil	1 per 100 tonnes

Appendix 1. (contd.)   Example of Typical Testing Rates for Sample Items of Roadworks

Process or Material	Purpose or Type of Test	Relevant Clause in D.Tp. Specification	Relevant Standard	Minimum Rate of Testing	Maximum Rate of Testing
Rolled Asphalt and Macadam Bases	Viscosity or Penetration of Binder		BS.76 BS.4690 BS.4691 BS.4692 BS.4693	1 sample per delivery, of which 1 in 3 for testing, remainder for reference	1 test per delivery
	Temperature of Mixed Material		BS.594 BS.4987	Every third load	Every load
	Grading and Binder Content	810 811 812	BS.598	1 per 150 tonnes for each plant	1 per 50 tonnes for each plant
Rolled Asphalt and Macadam Wearing Courses	Viscosity or Penetration of Binder		BS.4690 BS.4691 BS.4692 BS.4693	1 sample per delivery, 1 in 3 for testing, remainder for reference	1 per delivery
	Lake Asphalt Content			Every fourth blend (for lake asphalts, each blend must be tested)	Every blend
	Temperature of Mixed Materials		BS.594 BS.4987	Every third load	Every load

Appendix 1. (contd.)   Example of Typical Testing Rates for Sample Items of Roadworks

Process or Material	Purpose or Type of Test	Relevant Clause in D.Tp. Specification	Relevant Standard	Minimum Rate of Testing	Maximum Rate of Testing
Rolled Asphalt and Macadam Wearing Courses (contd.)	Full Design Mix Operation	918	BS.594	1 per scheme	1 per week
	Grading and Binder Content	907	BS.598	1 per 75 tonnes for each plant	1 per 25 tonnes for each plant
	Polished Stone Value of Aggregate		BS.812	1 per 10000 tonnes stone	1 per 1000 tonnes stone
Soil Cement	Minimum Temperature	702	—	—	—
	Grading	805	BS.1377	1 per 4000 sq.m.	1 per 1000 sq.m.
	Plasticity	805	BS.1377	1 per 4000 sq.m.	1 per 1000 sq.m.
	Degree of Pulverisation	805	BS.1924	1 per 4000 sq.m.	1 per 1000 sq.m.
	Sulphate Content	805	BS.1377	1 per 4000 sq.m.	1 per 1000 sq.m.
	Moisture Content	805	BS.1924	5 per 4000 sq.m.	5 per 1000 sq.m.
	Dry Density Insitu	805	BS.1924	5 per 800 sq.m.	5 per 800 sq.m.
	Specific Gravity		BS.1377	1 per 4000 sq.m.	1 per 1000 sq.m.
	Unconfined Compressive Strength, Dry Density re-moulded	2706	BS.1924	5 per 800 sq.m.	5 per 800 sq.m.

Appendix 1. (contd.) Example of Typical Testing Rates for Sample Items of Roadworks

Process or Material	Purpose or Type of Test	Relevant Clause in D.Tp. Specification	Relevant Standard	Minimum Rate of Testing	Maximum Rate of Testing
Soil Cement (contd.)	B.S. Compaction Test		BS.1924	1 per source	1 per 1000 sq.m.
Pavement Quality Concrete	Cement	1001–1024	BS.12	Weekly certificates	
	Water	1001–1024	BS.3148	None if from drinking water supply	
	Grading of Aggregates	1001–1024	BS.882	1 per day	3 per day or more frequently at first
	Moisture Content			At start of each day's work and when variation is suspected	Frequently (once per 20 m^3) if rapid fluctuations occur
	Workability		BS.1881	1 per 100 m^3	1 per 20 m^3
	Entrained Air		BS.1881	3 per 500 m^3	1 per 40 m^3
	Cores	1019/2709		6 from trial slab or early work to check compaction	10 per 1000 m. of carriageway when quality of concrete or compaction is suspected

Appendix 1. (contd.) Example of Typical Testing Rates for Sample Items of Roadworks

Process or Material	Purpose or Type of Test	Relevant Clause in D.Tp. Specification	Relevant Standard	Minimum Rate of Testing	Maximum Rate of Testing
Pavement Quality Concrete (contd.)	Indirect Tensile Test			1 pair of cylinders per 75 m. run of carriageway and 1 pair at start of day's work. At least 2 pairs per day	1 pair of cylinders per 75 m. run of carriageway and 1 pair at start of day's work. At least 6 pairs per day
	Dispenser for Air Entrained Agent			Daily, before start of concrete	
	Weight-batchers			Monthly certificate	
	Rigidity			All joints in trial bay	1 of each type of joint per day
	Alignment			All joints in trial bay	Every third joint
Reinforcing Steel	Tensile Tests			10 bars per structure	10 bars per structure
	Bend and re-bend Tests			10 bars per structure	10 bars per structure
	Analysis			1 sample per structure	1 sample per source

12 Supervision of construction overseas

D. J. LEE, BSc, DIC, FEng, FICE, FIStructE, Managing Partner, G. Maunsell & Partners, Consulting Engineers, London

SYNOPSIS. Whatever the quality of the Contract Documents, the capabilities of the contractor and the consultant supervisory staff, the supervision of work overseas may require a change of priorities and different skills from that familiar at home. This paper surveys some of these aspects with an emphasis on experience.

INTRODUCTION

The construction stage of any project is the most important. The construction sees the realisation of long cherished hopes or, in some cases, the shattering or tarnishing of long held beliefs. The successful realisation of a project cannot be achieved by the stroke of a pen on a Contract Document. It can only be won by the efforts of contractor and supervisors working together harmoniously towards the common end. The following attempts to review various aspects of this endeavour so that the client, the consultant and the contractor can all identify their role more clearly and thus assist the satisfactory realisation of projects for the common good.

CLIENT CONSULTANT RELATIONSHIPS

It might be expected that clients overseas range from the competent and well organised to the most obscure and inexperienced. In fact the U.K. consultant should never adopt a superior attitude because many overseas countries are better organised to get work done than is sometimes readily apparent in the home country.

The range embraces a technically based client employing competent, well trained and experienced staff familiar with all the issues of contract, programme, finance and design. The other end of the spectrum can be represented by a client who has a project in mind, not always with the money to realise it, and an immature and inexperienced staff briefed to bring policy into actuality. The pressure of development sometimes leads to the appointment by the client of young staff who have adequate overseas training but do not have the experience to convert academic solutions to practical achievement. Technical leadership is essential between the client

Supervision of Construction. Thomas Telford Ltd, London, 1985

159

and his consultant during the planning and pre-contract phases of a project because any decisions during those phases will inevitably have repercussions on the supervision phase.

Sensible clients know that time is money and enforce good discipline on all those concerned in programme decisions. The sensible client also makes a rational decision about the pre-tender design period but frequently this is too short and bids are called on incomplete drawings with inevitable repercussions on the bills of quantities and specifications. The contracts themselves demand a rigidly defined programme, with cost penalties if it is not met. The inter-action with specialists with other contractual design responsibilites is vital. On top of this the consulting engineer may be required to maintain rigorous budget control with reporting procedures throughout the detailed design phase. The fast tracking of projects requires exceptional management quality, particularly when the client quite rightly modifies his requirements in the light of changing circumstances.

On the other hand the less experienced client may be more suspicious of the motives of the consulting engineer who should be allowed freedom to advise and exercise skill and judgement. The consultant should not be placed unwillingly into adopting design specifications and standards devised for the developed world and which may not be best suited for the less developed countries.

A frequent difficulty stems from the fact that the client has not properly identified the task. Firm guidance is required at the briefing stage to define the project fundamentals. Very special demands are placed on staff in terms of their ability to state cases logically with diplomacy and patience.

The people appointed by the consultant to deal directly with the client should be selected for their personal qualities as much as for their technical competence. These consultants' representatives may be required to act with few supporting staff and to establish and manage a significant part of the overseas business of the firm. Some important points of policy can therefore be identified:-

(a) The independence and autonomy of those managing the consultant's overseas office and dealing with the client and his contractors must be defined. With safeguards it is appropriate that the guidelines are designed to stretch capacities rather than limit opportunities for overseas independence.

(b) The coordination of overseas independence must be matched by a flexible and understanding response from the head office of the firm at home.

(c) It is important that the personnel at various levels at home and overseas are compatible and maintain good communications and sense of understanding.

CONSULTANT TENDERER RELATIONSHIPS

International tendering may attract bids from organisations located in countries not previously active in the overseas construction scene. Contractors from Central and Eastern Europe, Latin America and Asia compete for work in countries where they may have had little or no prior experience. The consultant will have to exert effort to ensure that the tender documentation is understood and that the tender is soundly based. A natural assumption made by tenderers without much international experience is that what might be acceptable in their own countries is automatically likely to be acceptable in the overseas country. The consultant can be placed in a dilemma during the tendering stage when he realises that these considerations are likely to unbalance the tendering.

THE CLIENT TENDERER RELATIONSHIP

The client may or may not require the consultant to assist him with the adjudication of tenders and in recommending the appropriate award of contract. At all times the consultants duty is to the client and holds himself ready both at home and overseas to answer any questions and prepare any reports that may be required.

THE CONSULTANT CONTRACTOR RELATIONSHIP

Once a contract is let the consultant can only act in the best interest of his client. With the contractor's background and skills in mind the consultant attempts to effect the most successful conclusion for all concerned in terms of quality, programme and cost. This might involve the acceptance of amendments to suit the contractor's resources and experience. These in turn may involve construction techniques calling for changes in design details. For example a different approach to prefabrication (of steelwork or precast concrete), the design of temporary works and construction sequencing can all have a major impact on design and structural details.

Conflict may arise with the specification of construction materials in the contractor's home country and which may be imported for use in the project overseas. In some cases these arrangements are part of the financing deal. Logistics demand timely information to allow for the lengthy delivery times for such imports and a mutually constructive approach to solve these problems.

LIAISON AND COMMUNICATION

The demands of many overseas projects call for a full range of resources of a large design office where engineers and technicians are supported by specialists in the fields of survey, geotechnics, project management, measurement and estimating. These skills are nowadays supported and equipped with computers, word processing equipment and automatic draughting facilities. Sometimes it will be possible to base some of these resources overseas.

In other cases this may not be a practicable solution. Nevertheless it is important to ensure that decisions that are made overseas and in the design office at home are compatible.

An efficient system of communication between the design office and site based staff is necessary. Communication in this sense refers not merely to the provision of telex, telephone, and facsimile hardware but communication to all concerned in the project the problems and the actions that are to be taken to resolve them. If this is achieved it is possible to overcome the dangers which arise when design calculations and drawings are modified to meet changing circumstances that can arise during the course of the project. The author's firm has from experience developed several systems for organising and controlling the liaison process to handle the detailed circumstances applying in each overseas territory. The over-riding feature, however, is that the system has to be effective and disciplined. It must apply over the full range of the consultants services whether it be design, drawings, quantity surveying, measurements, specification and amendments, programme, construction methods and budget control.

Fundamentally a reliable system is based on a clear statement whereby responsibility is apportioned to one specific office selected to be concerned with a clearly defined activity whether this is production of drawings, calculations or contract supervision. That one office can then sanction design changes or other alterations for that element of work and the same office is responsible for compatibility with all other elements. As the project proceeds the responsible office may be redefined at various stages to suit the demands of the work most efficiently.

THE RESIDENT ENGINEER OVERSEAS

The level of supervision overseas can vary a great deal from that in the United Kingdom. It is not unknown for the client to cut by more than half the number of staff proposed by the consultant to be on site compared to U.K. projects. Generally overseas clients expect the Resident Engineer to be competent to advise in the fields of civil, structural, municipal, land, marine surveying, quantity surveying and contract management.

The client does not necessarily regard supervising staff as independent but expects him to be his guardian to the point of being unfair to the contractor. The professional independence of the Resident Engineer is not always accepted by the client on the basis that he who pays the piper calls the tune.

In some countries, the traditional role of the Resident Engineer is altered. The Resident Engineer himself may be an officer of the client and usually a citizen of the country concerned. The expatriate supervisory staff may be required to act as representatives on site in a technical capacity only. The Resident Engineer may deal with the administration of the contract itself but obtain technical advice from his expatriate counterpart, who is himself forbidden to correspond directly with the contractor. Contractually he is removed from the decision-making role and acts as a link between the Resident Engineer and the consultant.

Inspection work on site of temporary and permanent work is frequently left to local staff as part of the Resident Engineer's team and when occasionally the expatriate is required to carry out site inspection or checking he is not given authority to accept or reject work except through the Resident Engineer. Where the local language is used between Resident Engineer and the Client, there can be a time lag in the expatriate's knowledge of what is happening. Despite these possible shortcomings and frustrations to the expatriate, it has to be admitted that the system of local Resident Engineer with expatriate assistance has advantages to the developing country. It provides first hand experience for the local engineers and technicians in contract management and encourages them to take an active part in the decision process. Naturally expatriate staff have to be properly briefed before they take up such appointments.

PLANT, MATERIALS AND TESTING FACILITIES

Local conditions overseas may have significant influences on plant, materials and testing. The following remarks are derived from experience in Iraq to indicate some of the specific aspects and the distinction between these conditions and those in the U.K. A different set of conditions would apply to other countries.

Test Certificates

A specification may require the contractor to submit test certificates, furnished by the supplier or manufacturer of the material, and indicating compliance with the relevant standard.

In Iraq all cement and reinforcing steel was supplied by the client through a Government establishment but independent test results were not supplied. Samples of all delivered materials were therefore taken by the resident engineering supervisory staff within 24 hours of arrival on site for despatch to the Government testing laboratory.

Cement

Cement can be supplied from widely differing sources and on one project in Iraq cement arrived from Japan, Spain, Greece, Iraq and the Gulf and some of unknown origin bagged in Kuwait. Supplies were also sub-divided into sulphate-resisting and ordinary Portland Cement. The basic material therefore imposed problems in achieving quality control and appearance; one cement was light green in colour, and pressure on the testing laboratory involved a delay of up to 30 days, by which time much of the cement had been incorporated in the project. In other cases deliveries came in large batches as ships docked and provision of temporary additional weatherproof storage was required.

Reinforcement

Sources of supply of reinforcement were even wider than those for cement, where on one project steel came from Brazil, Argentina, Qatar, Spain, Japan, etc. all bundled to American standards. No steel was used before test results were to hand and so a tight control had to be exercised on bundle storage and registration of manufacturers identity marks.

Prestressing Strand

At the time of the supply of this material no suitable testing machine existed in Iraq. However the strand was supplied from Japan with complete test documentation and this was accepted.

Sand and Aggregate

High concentrations of gypsum occur in the area and close inspection of aggregates was necessary together with frequent soluble sulphate tests. One one occasion it was noted that the sand fraction coming from the crusher contained small white particles of pure gypsum which had not been dissolved when passing through the Archimedes Screw Washer. Supplies of sands from some sources had to be carefully monitored as sometimes the aggregate washing water is merely run into a reservoir to be reused thus increasing the saturation of sulphates in the water. One of the main problems for the contractor in supplying aggregates was the hard nature of the available raw material for crushing which rapidly wore the crusher jaws.

Testing Machines and Calibration

Where few machines for testing are available and one is giving trouble it is difficult to find an alternative to check the results. The supervisory staff is placed in the role of detective to make sensible decisions with the results.

Plant Supply

At a very early stage in the Contract a detailed list of all proposed plant must be submitted to avoid delays in the start of construction by shipment and custom clearance delays or for replacing unsuitable machinery. The contractor must usually be encouraged to order items supplied from outside the country well in advance of need. This reduces problems where remedial work, repairs and reordering lost or damaged parts have to be undertaken. The supervisory staff can be under intense pressure by the Contractor to accept material which is not precisely in accordance with the details and the specification because there has been late ordering or a delay in delivery. If changes of this type are accepted, it is vitally important that they are communicated to the consultant's office so that the implications of the adjustment can be judged.

Inspectors

Usually the availability of trained Inspectors is as limited as the availability of more senior staff and in order for these few to be effective they must be properly briefed with specific instructions as to what to monitor and to ask if in doubt about any operation.

Hot weather concreting

In summer in Iraq shade temperatures approach 50°C and the aggregate bays and the concrete batching plant act as heat storage areas. The specification may require concrete mix temperatures not to exceed 32°C and in the May to October hot season extra control is required on temperature measurement. Where concrete mix temperatures approach the maximum several simple methods can be used and which may be new to an inexperienced expatriate. The most effective method is the construction of horizontal shade screens above the bays and if this is done right at the beginning of the contract it is cost effective. Light water spraying can be effective but has some disadvantages, one being that the control of water in the mix proportions can be more difficult and also in dusty conditions silty particles can be washed down through the aggregate to form a sludge at the bottom of the storage bay.

The water storage tanks should be thoroughly insulated or buried below ground. Where tanks are overhead, they should be painted white as should cement silos. A simple water cooler working on the principle of latent heat of evaporation can be cheaply constructed on site. For large volumes of concrete proper water chilling plant may be necessary.

The batch truck mixer drums should be wrapped in hessian and watered some thirty minutes before use and kept damp during the pour. The batch plant should be situated so that haul times of more than thirty minutes are avoided.

The application of curing membranes on the finished concrete should be carried out as soon as practicable to reduce shrinkage cracking associated with concrete temperature rise.

LOCAL CONVENTIONS

Work supervision overseas is as varied as the countries themselves, the nationalities of those supervising the work, and the project technology. It should represent a challenge of great interest to the progressive expatriate. Difficulties experienced with works in the U.K. are likely to be the same to a greater or lesser extent overseas, together with the addition of other problems peculiar to that area. It is important that these local factors are borne in mind so that a sensible engineering balance is maintained. Large projects are likely to be of great interest as the opportunity for expatriate supervision is greater. Most Government clients employ their own in-house project management teams and overseas some of these teams include expatriates in the technical planning and administrative staff, although there is usually a conscious policy towards greater localisation. An exception may be the large multi-national corporations serving the oil industry and the like.

In the Gulf States many expatriates in Government employ are likely to be Egyptian, Pakistani, Sudanese or from other Islamic countries. In the Far East many Europeans are employed as well as a complex mix of local nationals. It has to be appreciated that at Client level, tact and understanding of nationals other than those of the host country is required. A good working relationship with all sectors of the administration will enhance the success of a project. Of course projects linked to international funding agencies are likely to involve technical input from expatriates of virtually any nationality.

Some clients can be autocratic. In Hong Kong for example, the conditions of contract may be easily recognised from UK practice, but at the same time the client retains significant powers. The engineer is given no authority himself to settle disputes between client and contractor. In theory all unresolved matters should be taken to arbitration but naturally in reality this has been overcome by the development of a tolerant relationship between client and contractor. At the present time British and Japanese contractors are successfully competing in Hong Kong as a result of the increasing complexity of some works. The contractor's expertise in these fields is putting the system to test. A change may be seen in contract administration with incentives for the contractor primarily aimed to assist construction progress and reduce the chance of arbitration.

DESIGN STANDARDS

Design standards overseas are generally based on early engineering experiences in the relevant area. In parts of the Middle East the oil industry has been influenced by Americans and design standards in that area may stem from this background. Supervisory staff must be cautious in attempting to apply the standards of his own country with which he may be familiar but which could be different from those usual in the country where he is working.

OVERSEAS CONTRACTORS

Contractors overseas fall into two broad groups - those that are local and those that are expatriate based. The local contractor, if sufficiently large, will employ management and specialist expatriate staff where local engineer expertise is short. The contractor is thus able to communicate well with consultant and client and many overseas contractors regard this as a most significant aspect of his employment of the expatriate.

The expatriate contractor who may be new to a particular market has to find a foothold and is thus either a specialist or sponsored by management policy or by his Government. As an example, Korean contractors can employ overseas Government sponsored labour from the ranks of those who have been given the choice to opt out of National Service. Korean contractors have thus been able to compete successfully in developing areas of the world and their example is likely to be followed by others.

LANGUAGE

Contract supervision requires that a common language of communication be adopted and the conditions of contract frequently state that only engineers competent in that language will be employed in positions of authority. It is necessary therefore that the smooth progress of work is assisted by good administration and recognised checking procedures.

Some expatriate contractors lack experience overseas but a balance has to be struck between the pressure of competitive bidding, and Government to Government understandings. It is effective for staff to learn a little of each other's language and customs. With good humour a rapport will build up which will stand them in good stead in the future.

Supervision has to be tolerant of the methods of working with which the contractor is familiar in his own country. This may have repercussions on safety and impose burdens in working out agreed construction sequences.

LOCAL CONSULTANCIES

Local design firms are being established in developing countries which after a suitable period for maturing themselves compete outside their own territories. The competition thus becomes keen for the Western consultant in the areas of language and local staffing. Associations with local firms may be helpful where there is a need for local supervision. In other cases the expatriate consultant may turn elsewhere than the local country for staff at a cost which is acceptable to the client. These enhance the problems with communications but have to be accepted in the interests of technology transfer.

CONCLUSION

The successful supervising engineer overseas will be of a stable personality and will attract others of a similar disposition around him. At a time of recession in the Western world it may be that an expatriate will view an overseas contract for various reasons as a relief and an escape from the restrictions of home. The consultant's interviewing techniques should be sympathetic to the potential staff member and his family, but should also establish the true motives for going overseas. Once appointed, particularly for Government projects, it is usually a worrying and cumbersome procedure to remove unsatisfactory staff from a contract.

Some postings are spartan, perhaps on a bachelor basis, in an unfamiliar and often uncomfortable climate. The employer should be sympathetic and compassionate to any emergencies arising either in health or family crisis. Wherever possible it is natural that husband and wife should remain together. In these circumstances it is approporiate that the characters of both be assessed before they are sent overseas. If the time of each of them is not fully and effectively used in business, sporting and social activities, then one or the other will be dissatisfied and affect the performance of the other. In some conditions it is natural to feel that only the more resolute could dependably perform their job of work.

Happily, from experience, there are large numbers of supervisory staff performing admirably for their firms and as ambassadors for their country. The author would like to salute them for their efforts.

13 A supervision brief

E. M. O'LEARY, BE, FICE, FIStructE, MIHT, MConsE, Senior Partner, Veryard & Partners, Cardiff

SYNOPSIS. A supervision brief is a communication document between the Engineer and his Representative on site. It should contain all the information and instructions necessary for the proper supervision of the Works but should in addition highlight those areas requiring special attention. The preparation of this brief should be a continuous process during design as it can influence design decisions.

INTRODUCTION

1. The idea of a prepared brief for those entrusted with the responsibility of supervising work on site is by no means a novel one. As recently as 1983 the Institution of Structural Engineers advocated the principle in a paper entitled - "Inspection of Building Structures During Construction". It refers to an inspection brief and sets out a detailed checklist of contents.

2. Inevitably these are mainly concerned with structural matters and are limited by definition to inspection. This present paper is intended, primarily, for civil engineering work carried out under the ICE Conditions of Contract, Fifth Edition and under the supervision of the Engineer's Representative or his site staff. It is not meant to deal directly with the work of supervision by the Contractor's staff although inevitably the two roles are closely related. A clearer definition of what is required of and by the Engineer's Representative may well benefit the Contractor's site staff.

OBJECTIVES

3. The role of the Engineer's Representative under the Contract is to "watch and supervise the construction, completion and maintenance of the Work". This is interpreted as being to ensure that the work is carried out to the standards of quality and to the timescale required by the Contract. The supervision brief should be drawn up to assist the Engineer's Representative to carry out his duties. With this in mind it should contain sufficient instruction to ensure that the correct information is available to the Engineer to enable him to discharge his various duties under

Supervision of Construction. Thomas Telford Ltd, London, 1985   169 the Contract and it should contain sufficient information to ensure that all crucial matters of design are translated to construction. The first of these two objectives is related to general matters and the second to the specific details of each contract.

INFLUENCE OF THE BRIEF ON DESIGN

4. Civil Engineering is an intensely practical activity in which the concepts of design and construction are inextricably linked. It is accepted that construction processes have a major influence on design. Insufficient attention is generally given to supervision at design stage and many site problems or disputes could be eased if the question – How can this be checked? – is asked during design. Tolerances or permitted deviations are common examples.

5. To ensure that such questions are asked and to gain maximum benefit from a supervision brief it is clearly necessary that it be drawn up during the design process and by the design team. Just as contract documentation is a conscious continuous process during the design stage so the supervision brief should be assembled from design decisions and not left as a final sweeping up operation when the Contract is let. By this means some problems of supervision which are in reality problems of construction may be avoided.

GENERAL CONTENTS OF THE BRIEF

6. Authority. The Engineer may, and usually does, extend the authority of his Representative to act on his behalf. The Contract requires that notice of such authority be given in writing to the Contractor. The supervision brief should start with a clear statement setting out in detail the delegated functions and powers of the Engineer's Representative.

7. This should be a detailed statement indicating the clause numbers where the Engineer's Representative may act on behalf of the Engineer. These delegated powers are usually wide ranging covering most aspects of the Contract with the exception of Clause 12(3), 44, 48, 60(3), 61, 63 and 66 – all excluded by Clause 2. Nevertheless a detailed statement is required and should be provided to avoid any misunderstandings.

8. The Engineer's Representative may in turn delegate functions to his assistants on site, but as these are likely to vary during the Contract they would not normally form part of a supervision brief.

9. Documentation and Filing. The supervision brief should contain a full, up-to-date set of the Contract Documents together with notes on the design office referencing and filing systems. The former are important in identifying amended drawings or instructions and the latter may avoid unnecessary delay in clearing correspondence.

Apparently innocent delays can often have significent cost implications when a Contract is in progress.

10.   Site Records. The object of most site records is to provide the Engineer with sufficient information to enable him to discharge his various duties under the Contract. The Engineer has frequently to make decisions which must be fair to both Contractor and Employer: Clauses 12(3) and 44 are examples. Such decisions can only be fair if the information on which they are based is correct and full. Proper site records may be the only information available and the importance of these cannot be overemphasised.

11.   It is surprising, then, that a standard format has not been agreed for these. Most organisations have developed their own and these take the form generally of a site diary, progress charts and the statutory accident report forms.

12.   The site diary is probably the single most important record of the activities on the site. This should give daily information on the following:

Weather −	temperature, maximum and minimum, wind velocity and direction, rainfall duration and intensity snow, frost, ice, fog.
Work in progress −	new work started work completed delays, progress
Manpower −	number by trades arrivals or departures
Materials −	deliveries tests and results removals
Plant & Equipment −	type and number on site
Visitors −	details
Administration −	instructions issued queries raised and replies given ordered variations issued approvals given memos issued telephone calls photographs taken

13.   Progress charts are best prepared using the approved programme as a base. It is best if this is prepared and agreed with the Contractor weekly to avoid disputes and disagreements building up and to enable the required action

to be taken by either side to remedy the situation.

14.   The importance of the Health and Safety at Work Act 1974 should be emphasised in the supervision brief. A copy of the statutory form contained in the Act should be included with the brief and the Engineer's Representative should be alerted to his own and the Contractor's responsibilities under the Act. The General Duties included in Sections 2 to 9 impose obligations on employers, employees and other personnel and these cannot be abrogated. The Department of Transport/County Surveyors' Society prepared in October 1980 Notes for Guidance in relation to the Act for work on motorways and trunk roads and this should be included in the supervision brief for work of this type.

SPECIFIC CONTENTS OF THE BRIEF

15.   The Design Concept.   The supervision brief should include a clear statement setting out the design concept. In the case of structures and buildings this should include, as a minimum, the design loading, the structural articulation and the principles of stability.   In retaining works the brief should include the design assumptions, the drainage proposls and the protection works necessary. Each project will require a specific statement to ensure that those responsible for supervision appreciate and can thereby ensure compliance with fundamental design principles. As with the rest of the brief this statement is best prepared during the design stage. By this means, it is hoped that matters vital to the design are not overlooked on site.

16.   Site Conditions. Although the contract documents should contain all available information on site conditions this information is frequently in precis form. The complete reports and file papers should be made available to the Engineer's Representative particularly in major earthworks contracts. Items which are fundamental to the design should be highlighted.   Details of all services should also be included.

17.   Setting out and Measurement. The Contractor is responsible for the correct setting out of the Works, but this is based on information supplied by the Engineer. The supervision brief should draw the Engineer's Representative's attention to any aspects of setting out which are more than usually crucial to the project.   Particular attention can then be paid to these during any site checks. This again is a matter which arises during design and the value of committing it to a supervision brief at that stage is an obvious one.

18.   Copies of relevant site photographs should also be included in the supervision brief to enable the Engineer's Representative to obtain the Contractor's agreement to these at the outset.

19.   Measurement is usually the responsibility of the Engineer's Representative although he normally requires the

attendance of the Contractor. It is vital, therefore, that the basis of mesurement is set out in the supervision brief. This is particularly important in earthmoving or landfill contracts where initial site contours have to be agreed at the outset.

20. <u>Programme.</u> Any matters which are vital to the programme of the work should be emphasised in the supervision brief. These may include traffic restrictions, the effects of tides, surface water discharge and flooding, agricultural management or local activities. Information on these matters relevant to the project should be drawn to the attention of the site supervisory staff.

21. <u>Materials or Services Ordered.</u> Full details of any materials or services ordered in advance of the Contract but forming part of it should be included in the brief. These should include the source, the delivery dates and acceptance or compliance criteria. Work to be carried out directly by the Employer should be similarly reported to the Engineer's Representative.

22. <u>Standards of Workmanship.</u> The attention of the supervisory staff should be drawn to those items where a particularly high standard of workmanship is concerned. Bridge bearings and joints are cases in point. Tolerances of setting out and quality of materials and workmanship are crucial to the proper performance of the bearings and joints. The supervision brief should record this.

23. Tolerances are too often quoted from earlier contracts and may not be intended or may not even be achievable. The designer who is aware that he has to advise site supervisors on crucial tolerances will probably view all tolerances in a more practical manner.

24. <u>British Standard Specifications.</u> The supervision brief should include a list of all British Standard Specifications and Codes of Practice quoted in the contract documents. Those which have a particular relevance to the Contract and which in the designer's opinion may be needed on site should be so marked and copies should be included with the brief.

25. <u>As Constructed Drawings.</u> The Engineer will require his Representative or site staff to either prepare or provide information for the as-constructed drawings. This work may have to start early on the programme and instructions on the preparation of the information should be included in the supervision brief.

SUMMARY OF CONTENTS

26. The following is a summary of those items which should be included in or covered by the supervision brief:

1. Authority   – a statement of the authority delegated by the Engineer to the Engineer's Representative.

2. Contract Documents — a full set of all contract documents issued.

3. Engineer's Filing System — list of all file references.

4. Site Records — blank books of all site records required by the Engineer.

5. The Design Concept — a concise description of the design concept highlighting any crucial matters.

6. Site Conditions — the complete report and files on any site investigations carried out.

7. Setting out — details of any setting out measurements which call for particular attention.

8. Measurement — information on the basis of measurement particularly in cut and fill work.

9. Programme — information on any matters which may affect or be affected by the programme.

10. Materials Ordered — details of any materials ordered in advance of the works.

11. Services by Others — details of any services to be provided by others e.g. by the Employer.

12.	Standards of Workmanship	–	information on standards of workmanship, including tolerances, which are of special significance.
13.	British Standard Specifications	–	a list of all British Standard Specifications quoted in the documents with copies of the more relevant Standards.
14.	As-Constructed Drawings	–	instructions to site staff on the information required of them.

CONCLUSIONS

27.   Good supervision will not only ensure that the quality of work is in accordance with the terms of the Contract but it may also help the Contractor in reducing the amount of rejected work.   Bad supervision, which is frequently the result of bad communications, benefits no one. The supervision brief is a communication document from the design office to the site.   If properly prepared it can greatly help the supervisory staff but its very preparation can influence design decisions to the benefit of the Employer.

Discussion on Papers 11–13

MR A. SANDBERG, Senior Partner, Messrs Sandberg, London

I entirely support a running assessment of results in whatever form it may be taken subject to the common sense point that one seriously bad piece of .work, such as a cracked weld, should not be passed over by statistics.

I recollect being involved in the construction of a concrete chimney and by the time four-fifths of the chimney had been completed the statistical requirements had been met, and the remainder could be completed without cement!

With regard to regulating payment according to results, we have been asked about this on many contracts but I have always thought that testing disputes are very time consuming and that any form of payment by graded results is asking for increased and duplicated testing and arguments concerning accuracy and, therefore, ultimately the overall result is non-productive. As I understand the Dutch method, they did not assess the testing and payments until completion of the contract which seemed a somewhat risky procedure in the event of there being something seriously wrong with the entire contract.

Quality assurance is good in so far as its intentions and hopefully its results are concerned but I have Mr Derrington's permission to quote his earlier remarks that paperwork is not the be all and end all. Taking a sensible approach, there has always been some form of quality control if not quality assurance, call it what you will, for contractors and suppliers and any major improvement must be good.

Nevertheless quality assurance is currently somewhat manufacture orientated and I do not think that there are many resident engineers or clients who will not want to know under their own auspices that they are obtaining compliance with the specification for the final end product in situ. If the Resident Engineer does not have his own laboratory facility he has lost the vital capacity to test what he wants when he needs it. There will always be human error, equipment and apparatus errors, pressures due to time and money, and to rely on any single method of control is not sufficient. This is not dissimilar to the Department of Transport's requirement for independent checks on bridge designs.

Supervision of Construction. Thomas Telford Ltd, London, 1985

177

MR R. MACKAY, Agent, Balfour Beatty Ltd, St Albans

I support the comments made by Mr Cearns about the suitability
of new technology methods – particularly the moisture
condition value test for testing the suitability of site
arising material – for use in construction projects – and hope
that the specifiers among the delegates to the symposium adopt
such tests for the future.

Where the specification does not precisely identify the
party (Contractor or Resident Engineer) responsible for the
classification of site arising earthworks material, who should
assume responsibility for that classification?

Mr Cearns: is it your opinion that since the material was
the Employer's, as it was generated within the Employer's
site, the Employer's specialist, i.e. the Resident Engineer,
should assume responsibility for the sampling and
classification of that material?

MR P. J. CEARNS

As the material was the property of the employer, it would be
normal for the Engineer to classify the material. However,
such classification would normally be subject to checks by the
Contractor, and it is therefore common, in such circumstances,
for the classification to be carried out jointly. It would
not be possible to be definitive on this matter without
reading the contract in question.

MR R. A. WEBB, Senior Project Designer, Dorman Long Bridge &
Engineering, Bedford

I would like to couple the topic of supervision overseas with
the discussion on health and safety and perhaps yesterday's
legal discussion as the Health and Safety at Work Act does not
necessarily apply overseas.

On a recent overseas bridge contract the consultant was
British, and the Contractor was from the local country. As
the contractors had no knowledge of erection of this type of
bridge they employed a British company as erection consultant.
This company worked out the erection scheme and temporary
works and wrote the erection memorandum, all of which were
approved by the consultant.

When it came to erection the local contractor went ahead in
conditions against the requirements of the memorandum, with
less staying than was required. Both the Engineer's
Representative and the Erection Consultant's Representative
instructed the local contractor to abide by the memorandum,
which he continued to ignore.

Although nothing happened, if it had, who would have been to
blame and if it had been in one of those countries where, as I
understand it, if you hire a taxi which has an accident then

the accident is your responsibility for having hired the taxi, who would then have been to blame?

MR D. J. LEE

Mr Webb has made a very important point about risk and liability overseas.

I firmly believe that supervision of construction is not a watertight activity divorced from all the other events of completing projects. This was why I referred broadly in my paper to all the aspects from the beginning of planning to the completion of the maintenance period. All will influence supervision.

In the situation cited it would depend in most countries on what was in writing and, most importantly, what the client would have done if the Contractor has precipitated a failure. If the supervising engineer has the confidence of the client then he is in a strong position to resist dubious practice. If there had been a failure it would clearly be consoling if the client fully backed up his Engineer against the Contractor.

It has to be remembered that overseas the health and safety of site operatives is not always regarded as paramount nor are the operatives themselves aware of the importance of safe working. Nevertheless I have been impressed in recent years with the improvements in safety and welfare of personnel on site. No UK-based supervisor should imagine that injuries or fatal accidents will be treated lightly overseas by the authorities concerned or he will regret taking such an attitude. Integrity and tactful behaviour by the supervisor will usually stand him in good stead in emergencies. If he has the good opinion of workmen and others on site they will seek to protect him from unreasonable consequences.

MR C. BIGGIN, Project Engineer, Watson Hawksley, High Wycombe

Would Mr Lee (and possibly Mr Deuce and Mr Sweetapple) comment on the need for the Engineer to give a greater degree of support for and communication (at the outset) with the Engineer's Representative on site on overseas contracts. Very often, owing to the nature of the posting, the Engineer will have to delegate more of his powers than normal to the Engineer's Representative who will more often than not be less experienced than his counterpart supervising a UK contract of similar size and yet will be expected and required to assume greater responsibility in dealing with both the Contractor and the client.

MR D. J. LEE

I agree that the duties and delegated powers of the site
representative of the Engineer should be clearly set out in
writing before starting the tour of duty in addition to
general briefing.
   Your comment certainly confirms the remarks made in my
paper.

MR P. A. FITZPATRICK, Fitzpatrick & Son Ltd, Hoddesdon

Mr Lee: do you think that the higher status of the Engineer
abroad is affected only by his personality – for they are all
considered the equal of a doctor in this country (who is
revered in the UK).
   Do you agree that the effectiveness of a resident engineer
(like a site agent) is in inverse proportion to the square of
the distances from his head office.
   Why was night concreting omitted as a means of reducing
heat problems – it is a regular procedure in south and west
USA.

MR D. J. LEE

The enhanced status of an Engineer abroad is both a pleasure
and a responsibility. I see it as assisting in the long term
the raising of the Engineer's status at home as well. Modern
methods of communication are so diverse and efficient that the
distance of a site from the head office is not such a problem
as it used to be. Of course some areas can be cut off but we
are in regular communication with all our site personnel on a
very regular basis.
   I agree that night work can assist many site activities
affected by heat problems. Usually in Iraq an early start is
made at first light.

MR E. JAMES, Senior Lecturer, Hatfield Polytechnic

With projects in the Third World (e.g. small water supply
projects) it is vital to investigate the maintenance at the
feasibility study stage.
   The maintenance team should then be trained and budgeted for
during the design and construction stage of the project.
   The locals should therefore be fully involved at the
feasibility, design, construction and maintenance stages.

MR R. FREER, Engineer, Pencol Engineering Consultants, London

Before the 100 of us here separate and leave I should like to
ask you Mr O'Leary, as chairman of the organizing committee,

what your committee intends to do next to develop the ideas we have expressed to produce a record of good practice that we can work up.

Common sense and common interest both encourage us to try to interpret contracts in the sense described as honourable rather than narrow and legalistic and some of us are aware of a sense of overbearing bureaucracy which is preventing us from doing so. I suggest that your committee might be able to reverse this trend and to initiate new guidelines which restore some of the common sense and personal satisfaction to site construction and supervision.

MR E. O'LEARY

It is the intention of the Structural Engineering Group Board to discuss the idea of producing a guide of good practice in the supervision of construction work at its next meeting. This, hopefully, will contain the practical points highlighted at this symposium and I, personally, would very much welcome the inclusion in it of standard forms such as site diary reports, a supervision brief checklist, ordered variations, Engineer's instructions etc.

MR J. DALLAWAY, Supervision Manager, Ove Arup Partnership, London

I request that JCT contracts and supervision under them be given consideration in any future supervision guide prepared by the ICE.

DR N. M. L. BARNES, Martin Barnes & Partners, Stockport

It is the Contractor's men who do the work of which the quality is to be supervised; therefore it is the Contractor's own foremen and supervisors who are most concerned in the problem. Would it not be. a good idea to monitor the Contractor's plans for supervision, not just to wait for bad work to be done and then to condemn it?

I reinforce an earlier point that the law in the UK at the moment hinders practical supervision as discussed today. Can the ICE use its influence to initiate a change?

MR A. SANDBERG, Senior Partner, Messrs Sandberg, London

Following Dr Barnes's comments on discussing quality control with the Contractor at an early stage in the contract, ideally this should be done with the short-listed contractors before letting the contract while the client is still in a controlling position. On one contract we interviewed the

three lowest tenderers to confirm that they were going to
follow the compliance requirements of the specification with
regard to materials, and it was explained that these were
going to be rigorously enforced to avoid any misunderstanding.
On this occasion the lowest tenderer withdrew, basically on
the grounds that he did not anticipate that the specification
would be adhered to.

Mr Cearns says in fact that we were asking for the
Contractor's quality assurance procedures before recommending
him for the contract. I agreed, but quality assurance was not
officially in existence at that time, and all that was
required of the Contractor was that he should comply with the
requirements of the specification.

MR R. F. HUGHES, Director, Property Services Agency, Croydon

I would like first of all to quote from the works' diary of
the Agent and Clerk of Works to the Duke of Marlborough during
the extensions of Marlborough House in 1770.

'I am obliged to get the work done at Marlborough House when
the workmen please and not when I wish to have it nor when it
ought to be done.

'The slater was prevented by the negligence of the plumber
from pointing his work more than a month and the plasterer,
under pretence that the slating was not done, neither sent in
his stuff nor made the least preparation for beginning. I was
therefore compelled to make them all fall to work at the same
time or else God knows when it would be done.'

Present methods of supervision of construction are not
wholly adequate especially with regard to the civil
engineering aspects of building works where there may be a
Site Architect and Clerk of Works but no Resident Engineer.
This is possibly because of the different views taken of site
supervision by the Architect and the Engineer. Where the
Architect is the lead consultant, which is normal for building
work, he normally deals with the client over the matter of
site staff. It is often overlooked that on average 60% of the
time taken in the construction of buildings involves the work
of the civil engineer.

The present system is also not adequate because it is not
possible for a small team of supervisors to embrace all the
aspects of the work. M & E work in particular suffers from
this problem. A further problem is that the Clerk of Works
may become an apologist on behalf of the Contractor. Close
working and sharing of site facilities leads to a softening of
attitudes particularly where extensions of time are involved.

It has been suggested that from certain works we would be
better off without Engineer's site staff. Contractors lean on
the Engineer's supervisory staff and depend on them for
quality control. The relative responsibilities become

difficult to assess in the event of a dispute.

The Contractor is usually under pressure to keep his site supervisory staff to a minimum. In times of heavy demand good site supervisors are in short supply, particularly those in the front line when craftsmen pay too high, trade union activity is also high, and there is no incentive for suitable craftsmen to become supervisors. In times of low demand tender prices are keen and contractors look to keep supervisory costs as low as possible, at times lower than acceptable.

Could it be that with the growth of quality assurance schemes – third–party schemes for cement and steel reinforcement have recently been launched and there is a trade scheme for ready–mixed–concrete – that we should look towards quality assurance for contractors?

As a first step could Engineers not specify the level and discipline of the key supervisory staff the Contractor is to provide. Could they not then call on the Contractor to provide certificates of compliance for the various stages of work? This would give contractors an opportunity to maintain an improved level of site supervisory staff against a turn-round in demand. Such a system would not preclude site visiting by the Engineer to check on the works at appropriate stages nor would it preclude parallel testing of materials and components.

If we cannot go this far perhaps we can look at an intermediate solution as I think the responsibility for supervision has moved too much out of the hands of the Contractor into the hands of the Engineer.

MR D. DENNINGTON (CHAIRMAN)

Closing remarks

It is my pleasant duty to make a few closing remarks to summarize the symposium.

The first notable feature has been the wide range of discussion to which the whole subject has given rise.

To some degree supervision has been accepted and discussed, and the object has been overlooked – I have the view that in a perfect world it should be unnecessary and to this end I like to ensure that the 3% additional cost represents value for money to the employer with regard to the whole cost of a project – probably this is a subject in itself.

At first I was concerned that this symposium may have lost sight of the reason for our discussions but this soon proved not to be the case.

It would be invidious to select particular papers for comment but it is interesting to classify them – not by content, which was arranged by the conference organizers, who gave us a very balanced selection, but by style.

The papers of Mr Sweetapple, Mr Cearns and Mr O'Leary are

what I call library papers to which we shall be grateful to refer and also to quote.

Mr Abrahamson, Mr Royce and Mr Weddell also mix opinion and advice in a helpful manner.

The specialist view on insurance has been provided by Mr Griffiths and Mr Cottam has similarly told us of his experience with the important management contract now being employed on many schemes.

Dr Barnes has reminded us of the wider implications of supervision which cannot be confined to a check on workmanship.

Finally, Mr Lee has dealt with the all-important side of export engineering, adding to Mr Sweetapple's experience, and Mr Deuce, Mr Fitzpatrick and Mr Shipp have given us strong views from their positions in what is really one profession and this latter point is what I think has come over very strongly. We have aired many different opinions at this symposium but in all instances we have recognized how we all draw together to achieve a good job on time and within the contract sum. Good will is still a vital ingredient of contracts.

There are many further comments I should like to add but the proceedings of the symposium will say this better.

I allow myself just one comment: training has been referred to and I have been informed that five members of the symposium have applied for certificates of attendance to qualify for their 1.5 Chilver days for the PE2 course which this meeting represents. This is heartening and shows that we are disseminating our knowledge in width and depth as a learned society should. I know it will be of interest to Mr Derrington, our Vice-President, who opened the symposium and who is also chairman of the Institution's education and training committee.